Christ at the Coffee Shop

A Collection of Short Stories

By

Nathan Ingram

Tranquility Ranch Publishers

Magnolia, Texas

2005

ISBN# — 0-9747425-1-1

Tranquility Ranch Publishers
25796 Tranquility
Magnolia, TX 77355

Project Coordinator — Rita Mills
Cover Design — Gladys Ramirez
Text Design — Rita Mills
Editor — Peggy Stautberg

The paper used in this publication meets the requirements of the American National Standard for Permanence of Paper for Printed Library Materials Z39.48-1984.

Printed in the United States of America

Author's Note

Unless otherwise noted, all Bible quotations are from the *New American Standard Bible*, copyright 1960, 1962, 1968, 1971, 1972, 1973, 1975, 1977, 1995 by The Lockman Foundation.

Used by permission. www.Lockman.org.

Some—but not all—of these stories are true. The ones that are true depend upon my memory for their accuracy, so some will no doubt contain errors. The goal of this book is to inspire the reader to extract relevant and powerful truths from the stories in order to make God visible within the ordinary.

Table of Contents

Stories

Acknowledgments

To Roger Cadwalder, DVM, DrPH, mentor and partner. Thank you for amazing me every day with your uncanny ability to discover godly significance in commonplace events.

To Jerry Laird, faithful co-worker, good friend, and dedicated man of God. Thank you for helping me understand that my bread isn't quite done, but it is OK with God.

To Burton and Laura Ingram, my father and mother. Thank you for your marriage to each other, your tireless work for the family, your ceaseless encouragement and your belief that I could write a book.

To David and Nancy Lunceford, my wife's parents. Thank you for your daughter and your acceptance. You never once hinted that I wasn't good enough, and that has made all the difference.

Last, but really first, to Lindy Ingram, my wife. It would take another book to say it all, but let me say this: I sure do love you.

Introduction

I tried to draw the air once, but nobody recognized it. That's not surprising, though, because it is difficult to make unseen things visible.

Take God, for example. I can't draw God because I don't know what He looks like. He is an abstraction, challenging me to search for common denominators that will fit into my limited experience as I try to become familiar with Him. As part of my quest I look for God where I am, in settings that are familiar, among people with whom I have things in common.

The Bible says, "We know that in everything God works for the good of those who love Him" *(Romans 8:28)*. That being true, it must be that God works in everything, including the ordinary.

By looking for God in the ordinary, then, I find it extraordinarily amazing, and quite delightful, to find Him. Not face-to-face, but indirectly, subtly interwoven into the fabric of everyday events.

I find God in the commonplace. He is on the roads, in the stores, in my home, and at the coffee shop. The spiritual is hard to understand, except as it is manifested in the unremarkable. It is fitting, then, that Christ would be in a coffee shop. At one time He was at home in a carpenter's shop, at parties, on the lake (literally) with friends, and walking through the farmers' fields. Why not at a coffee shop as well?

I hope that this brief work will help you envision God in common places, just as swaying fields of grain and ripples on the water capture the reality of the air around us. And realizing this truth, may you be joyfully refreshed and aware that God in heaven knows something about common folk and in knowing, deeply cares.

Christ at the Coffee Shop

> **"**I walked into Starbucks® in time to catch the tail-end of a devotional.**"**

———•◦•———

Christ At The Coffee Shop

I interrupted a worship service this morning, but I didn't mean to. My mind was set on a cup of coffee and a slice of banana nut bread to fill my stomach, but what I got was even better. It filled my soul.

My arrival there at 6:30 in the morning was not on purpose. I had set the alarm for 6:30, thinking I would get up and go study awhile before work. I awoke before the alarm went off, showered, and then checked the clock. I had gotten up at 5:30. Might as well stay up and study a little longer.

As a result, I walked into Starbucks® in time to catch the tail-end of a devotional. It looked like there were about

about twenty-five in attendance. I thought they were a school study group, so I asked the coffee clerk what the subject matter was. "It's a bunch that meets in here every Tuesday. Some kind of religious thing." I was intrigued and wanted to know more.

All of them were in high school; about the same number of boys as girls. The girls did the talking: "It's like, God is so cool and everything, and we, like, need to glorify Him and like, be thankful and everything." The speaker was a pretty seventeen-year old. She would have fit on a cheerleading squad or the student council. She apparently had the consent of the group to be their leader. She played a worship song on her CD player, said a few more words, sang some songs with the group, took prayer requests, and dismissed the assembly.

Her name was Sheila. She introduced herself to me and I asked her the name of her group. "Well, we're just kids." She hadn't lived long enough, yet, to learn eloquence with the adult race. "We're from three different schools and we meet here every Tuesday morning." A nervous laugh, a shifting of the feet, and an awkward silence followed. "Sorry if we disturbed your quiet."

She didn't know exactly what to say or how to act because I was a stranger. She was eager but shy, kind of like a baby animal—say, a lamb. Then she saw my open Bible on the table and her eyes lit up with recognition. We both had the same shepherd, so I wasn't a stranger after all. We talked a couple more minutes, and then she left.

Ten minutes later the coffee shop was empty, the chairs neatly arranged, the carpet clean and the tables nearly spotless. It was almost as if nobody had been there, but not quite. Still lingering among the earthy smells of coffee and bread was the unmistakable, inexpressibly delightful aroma that I have now come to associate with Jesus Christ *(II Corinthians 2:15).*

"On an impulse I dropped to one knee. "Come here, Boy." I hooked him with one arm and dragged him to me, all thirty-five pounds of stiff, proud, resentful little boy."

———◦•◦———

Monster Power

"I want a drink." There was nothing wrong with the request, except that this was the fifth time in twenty minutes and he was supposed to have been asleep half an hour ago. But there he stood, all four years of him, like the Rock of Gibraltar in the middle of the hallway, arms folded, face clouded with a scowl.

I was mad. I had already used up a lot of my patience during the first four drink episodes, and now I was all out. This little person was disobeying me and I wasn't going to allow it. I spanked him. Now that should do it.

Two minutes later he was back in the hall, same posture, same request. I couldn't believe it. Who did he think he was, anyway? Didn't he know that I was the boss? Of all the persistent four-year-olds I had ever seen, this one took the prize.

I stood looking down at him in helpless frustration. He didn't quite come up to my waist. His favorite pajamas, the striped pink and white ones, were still too big for him. I made a mental measurement. Yeah, he was a lot smaller than I was. I wondered what I looked like to him.

On an impulse I dropped to one knee. "Come here, boy." I hooked him with one arm and dragged him to me, all thirty-five pounds of stiff, proud, resentful little boy. I hugged him to me and it was like hugging a board. The scowl didn't go away.

"Listen, do you know what?"

He didn't.

"I can see that you don't want to go to bed, but I'm telling you that even if you don't want to, I sure do love you and I'm really glad that I get to be your Dad."

The rock crumbled. Molten tears flowed. His body relaxed into my arms like a weary traveler finding rest. "Daddy, every night a wolf chases me."

Oh…. Let's see how that one goes over in the next parenting seminar. "What do you do when your child is afraid of a wolf? You spank him." I felt smaller than he was.

"Well, boy, tonight when he comes after you, you pick up a big stick, and go toward him and you tell him, 'Now look here, wolf, you'd better leave or I'm going to bonk you right on the nose. And if I can't whip you, my Dad is right behind me, and he'll come and beat you up.'"

The tears dried. He grinned. He was asleep in two minutes.

The next morning he was up and busy, getting dressed for daycare. I asked him, "Caleb, how did you sleep?" He looked at me like I had asked one of the dumbest questions possible.

"Fine."

A few minutes later, after I thought he had forgotten, he said, "I beat him up."

"What?" It was my turn to be puzzled. "I beat him up, Dad. I beat the wolf up." Well … I was amazed, but I shouldn't have been. What are dads for, anyway? Part of their job is to take on monsters so the kids can feel safe, knowing that they don't have to face the wolves on their own.

Dads, you have power over your kids' monsters. Are they in the closet? Shut them up in there, or expose them. Are they under the bed? Yell at them and make them get out. Are they in dreams? Join in the dreams and play backup to the hero kid. You have the power. Use it.

By the way, I have monsters. I really get scared when I think I have to fight them by myself. I'm afraid the wolves will get me. I'm worried the marriage won't last, or the mortgage won't get paid, or the car will break down, or the job will dry up. My day is full of monsters. The wolves are snarling and scratching.

Then I remember, and I grin, and I fall asleep. I don't have to face them alone. Oh, I know, in this world I will certainly have monsters, but I can take heart, because He who walks with me has overcome the world *(John 16:33)*. He has monster power. His name?

Jesus.

"Have you known the excruciating loneliness of realizing that those who know you best, don't know you at all?"

———•◆•———

If You Know The Who

He had it all.
Then he lost most of it and didn't know why.

His wife wanted him to blame God. His friends cried, "Foul," and told him to repent of whatever he had done to bring such bad luck upon himself. He got very sick and wanted to die. These were dark days for Job.

He had been a great man. Plenty of livestock, a big family, respected in the community. That was before the big cosmic meeting.

The sons of God convened and the devil attended. The devil accused God of unfair play, especially when it came to Job. God gave the devil some leeway and he took advantage of it.

Have you read Job? He lost 7,000 sheep, 3,000 camels, 500 yoke of oxen, 500 female donkeys, all but a handful of his servants and his ten children, all in one day!

Job didn't respond the way the devil wanted him to, so at the next big meeting Satan begged God for permission to do more damage. Shortly thereafter, Job lost his health. Infected sores riddled his body. That's when his ill-advised friends came to see him and his wife told him to die.

Job wanted to know *why*. Wouldn't you? When bad things happen in your life, don't you think you could bear them better if you only knew why—if there was some bigger purpose that you could understand? How about the car accident that claimed the lives of two teenagers? The fever that took the baby? The business deal that never happened? The promise that was never kept? Broken expectations and crushed dreams. We wish someone would tell us why.

Job didn't know about the heavenly meetings. He didn't see the bigger picture. He was just living his life, and suddenly catastrophe struck his household. No one can blame him for wanting to know why.

His friends tried to tell him why, but they were wrong. They thought that Job had done something evil, and needed to confess it and repent of it so that God could help him.

Sometimes friends are like that. They analyze your problems and give advice, but they might be mistaken.

Job's friends were of no comfort to him, because they incorrectly interpreted his pain. Job told them so, which made them really mad. I can see them now. "Look at him, lying there in filth and rags, claiming to be righteous! If he is so righteous, then why is he in the shape he's in? Anybody with a lick of sense knows that God doesn't let something like this happen to a righteous man."

Have you ever had that happen to you? Have you known the excruciating loneliness of realizing that those who know you best don't know you at all? Don't you sometimes want to appeal to a higher court, to someone who really does understand your problem?

So did Job. He appealed to the highest court, saying, "Oh that I knew where I might find Him... I would present my case before Him" *(Job 23:3-4)*.

He got his appointment. Only, God came directly to Job.

Yes, God came, but it wasn't on Job's terms.

"Who is this that darkens counsel by words without knowledge?" *(38:2)*. God Himself was questioning Job. A rough opening remark to a man in great pain, wouldn't you agree?

It didn't get any better after that. In fact, Job hardly

had a chance to talk at all, because God was asking the questions. "Where were you when I laid the foundation of the earth? Tell me, if you have understanding ... have you ever in your life commanded the morning, and caused the dawn to know its place? Is it by your understanding that the hawk soars? Is it by your command that the eagle mounts up? Will the faultfinder contend with the Almighty?" You can read it for three chapters, God questioning Job.

When God finished, Job got his chance. Now he had his opportunity to find out why. He could really get to the bottom of his problems now. What are you going to say, Job?

What would *you* say? Wouldn't you have your list all made out, your questions worded precisely? After all, this would be a once-in-a-lifetime opportunity.

What did Job say? Not what you would expect.

"I have declared that which I did not understand, things too wonderful for me which I did not know ... I have heard of You by the hearing of the ear; but now my eye sees You; therefore I retract, and I repent in dust and ashes" *(42:3-6)*.

What!? Here's your chance, Job. Are you crazy? What do you mean, you take it back? Here's your big opportunity and you are blowing it!

Did Job blow it? Maybe not.

Job wanted to know why, but the answer he got was

more important than the question he had asked. Job didn't get his answer, but on the other hand, he got all the answers he would ever need.

God restored the fortunes of Job, only this time he had twice as much. Ten more children were born to him, he had more livestock, and he lived 140 more years *(42:12ff)*. As far as I know, he never learned why he'd suffered as he had, but that was fine with Job. He didn't have to know why, because he now knew God.

You see, the "why" question can't be answered with words because it's an inappropriate question. The real answer is not found in an answer; it is found in a relationship. Job didn't know the "why," but he found he didn't have to, because he knew the "Who." He knew God. He had learned the true answer to his problems—the only answer that satisfies.

If you know the "Who," you can endure the "What" without having to know the "Why."

" I thought it was a fine expression of creative talent, but the old man wasn't into art. **"**

—•◦•—

The Old Man And The Shovel

The old man had been known to give us boys a few lickings from time to time over what we considered trifling matters. Mostly it was about money, or more likely, our lax attitude toward it. Money must have been hard to get in those days, because the old man sure took it personally when any of us did something that cost him. I distinctly recall the stinging belt one time when I made a pretty design on the dirt stable floor with expensive sweet feed that was reserved for the milk cow. I thought it was a fine expression of creative talent, but the old man wasn't into art.

He was stern, sure enough, maybe above what he should have been, and we grew to hold more than a little fear and respectful regard for him. We didn't want to get on his bad side.

Of late, though, he seemed to be going a little soft. We knew he spent a lot of early morning hours sitting in his easy chair Bible-reading and contemplating, but we weren't sure what all that meant. One day we found out.

Mike had one speed: wide open. He pushed everything to the limit and then generally took it on over the edge. He ought to have died several times but God probably had a special hyperactive angel on his case. He tried everything—some things twice—but mostly what he tried was the old man's patience.

He should have known the tractor was too little for the log, especially after looking at the hill where he had to drag it. We were on the creek bottom and had cut down a hemlock tree that was about to be undercut by the creek waters and fall down. This tree was mighty big for this part of Tennessee. Two grown men could barely reach around it and touch hands. The first limb was way up the trunk. The trunk went up forever. We had sawn the log into sawmill lengths, and then planned to drag them up the hill with the little Massey Ferguson tractor and load them onto the wagon.

Mike was the driver and he figured he could do it. There wasn't much of anything that we could say to make him see it otherwise. He said that he would hitch to the log just right, get a good running start before he hit the hill, and that he knew it ought to go right up, no problem.

Wrong. He got a good running start on it, but when the tractor hit the slope, instead of going on up the hill as planned, it reared and swung its front end around and came down on the shovel, breaking the handle clean in two.

Time stood still there for a minute. Shovels cost money. The old man hadn't seen it, but he would pretty soon. We were all looking to witness some fireworks when he did. None of us wanted to be Mike.

In a few minutes there he came, hickory walking stick in hand, winding through the huckleberry and Virginia Creeper, checking on our progress; he was always big on progress. Wanted things done now.

After a couple of eternities, he made it up to the scene of the accident and stood looking, taking it all in with X-ray eyes that viewed the picture behind the picture. He saw our expressions and then read our thoughts. He took in the sideways tractor, the too-big log, the broken shovel and—no surprise here—the driver. His mouth dropped a bit at the corners and his eyes squinted just a little. Then, he turned around and started walking off.

We figured he was too mad to be in his right mind

and was probably just addled. We were purely mystified at his reaction. The quickest belt in east Tennessee should have already been drawn and swung. Ordinarily, by now we'd have been cringing under the money-doesn't-grow-on-trees lecture and the grow-up-and-get-responsible speech. But we didn't get any of it. He just walked away.

A brave one among us found his voice and called out, asking if he wasn't going to do anything to Mike on account of the shovel. The old man paused for a minute, called back a brief reply, and then walked on.

These days, my brother Mike spends a lot of early morning hours sitting in his easy chair Bible-reading and contemplating. He heard the answer that day and credits the old man for showing him God in just one sentence:

"The boy is worth more than the shovel."

"Two pigs in a mud puddle don't condemn each other for being dirty. If one of them gets clean it's because someone pulls him out . . . ."

The Million-Dollar Beggar

S ir, could you spare one million dollars?"
   The request came from a man sitting on a bench at the bus stop. Shabby coat, shabby shoes, shabby hair. The only thing neat about him was his smile.

I was just walking by and he picked me out. He asked the question with unabashed ease. No begging for eighty-five cents to catch the bus, or fifty cents for a cup of coffee, or a quarter for a phone call. No sir, this man was different; he was a possibility thinker.

I stopped in amazement. I had never had someone ask me for a million dollars before.

The concept of the begging man himself wasn't new

to me; people are often asking me for money. Time spent near downtown Houston has exposed me to a fairly steady stream of humans whose sole purpose in life seems to be finding me in a crowd and telling me how poor they are and, by the way, do I have some money that they could have?

I've never really known if my response to them is right or wrong. Have you ever had that dilemma?

One man on a corner wears a well-worn sign that says he will work for food. Another one's banner reads, "Hungry, homeless, veteran. Please help. God bless you." The same people stand on the same street corners, day after day.

What do you do with these people? Do you give them money? If you do, do you feel right about it? Or maybe you don't give them money. Are you satisfied that you were correct? Maybe you just ignore them, as I do. How does that feel?

The problem of beggars on street corners has plagued me for a long time. I couldn't feel right about giving them anything, and I couldn't feel justified in not giving them something. Usually, I ended up getting angry with them for being there, unwelcome and uninvited, invading my conscience. It wasn't polite of them. They needed to mind their own business, which did not include trying to make me feel guilty. Sound familiar?

Now here was a beggar asking me for a million dollars. I didn't know what to say.

"A million dollars?"

"Please."

Well, at least he was polite about it.

What was I to do?

Jesus told a story to His followers because they were confused about how to treat other people—especially offensive people. They asked Jesus to clarify. Instead of answering the question, He told them a story. You can read it in Matthew 18.

A king had a servant who owed him ten million dollars. The servant couldn't pay, so the king decided to sell the servant and all the servant's family. The servant fell at the king's feet and begged him for more time, saying that he would pay it all. (That's optimistic. Ten million dollars?!).

The king had compassion for the begging servant and forgave him the entire debt. Notice he forgave him. He didn't put the servant on a payment plan. No zero-down-and-zero-interest-until-32 AD. No Chapter Eleven reorganization. None of that. When the king was finished, it was as if the servant had never owed him a penny. Wiped clean. Completely free from obligation. *Forgiven.*

What are the chances of that happening? Perhaps one in ten million? Maybe less, but it happened to me.

I am like the forgiven servant. I was in deep poverty of spirit, desperately in need of a Savior. I was in debt way over my head (at least ten million dollars' worth), drowning in the mire of my own depravity. Jesus forgave my debt, not because He owed it to me, and not even because I asked Him to, although I did ask Him to. He did it because He wanted to.

This scraggly man, this requester of a million dollars, is not so different from me. We, in fact, have something in common.

We are both beggars.

What's the difference between begging for money and begging for forgiveness? The difference is minimal because we both need something we don't have.

Do you know why the beggar asked me for a million dollars? I think I do. It's because he didn't know what he really needed, so he just asked for money. I couldn't expect him to say, "Sir, could you spare some self-respect?" Or, "Sir, could you give me someone who will love me unconditionally long enough for me to make it back up?" Money was a lot easier to ask for than the things he really needed, so that's what he asked for. Should I be critical, then, and angry with my million-dollar beggar?

I wonder why Jesus told that story about the king and the servant. I don't know the whole reason, but I am convinced that part of it is because He knew I would be offended at presumptuous beggars who didn't know what they needed, and who asked me for the wrong things. And, being so easily offended, I needed a Biblical reminder that I, too, am a beggar.

Two pigs in a mud puddle don't condemn each other for being dirty. If one of them gets clean, it's because someone pulls him out of the dirt and washes him off. He couldn't do it on his own. In the same way, if Jesus had not done what He did, I would still be dirty, so there is no room for superior attitudes here.

What, then, am I to do with beggars? I still don't know, exactly. Maybe later I will have the whole answer, but for now I can only say that I am to be gentle with them. If I can meet their needs, I should. Neither they nor I know what we really need, and no doubt we often ask for the wrong things.

The truth is that this man and I live in two different worlds, and to all appearances we don't have much in common. It is easy for me to be angry with him because he does things I don't think he should, but remembering my true position before God helps me with that.

I'm a beggar, too.

"The homely worm becomes a butterfly. The ugly duckling becomes a swan. The little seed becomes a rare blossom, and my children become perfect."

———•◦•———

Smuggling Cats

The rule was clear: no cats in the house.

The Ingram family had five new additions: the cat's litter of kittens. Three-year-old Carter couldn't keep her hands off them. They were the neatest things she had seen in her short life. They were a lot better than stuffed animals because they would meow on their own, lick her face, and wriggle around. She begged to bring the new arrivals up to her room in order to rescue them from the fearful dangers of the garage.

All her pleading fell on deaf ears. I stood firmly opposed to the move. I didn't think the garage was all that scary for little cats so I refused them entry into the house.

Carter's wailing gradually subsided as she resigned herself to the fact that her Dad was boss. She trudged past me in the kitchen, making the journey to the garage with shuffling feet and a gloomy face. I had won. I was satisfied.

Five minutes later she was back, moving quickly, furtively. My suspicious eye detected a bulge around her waistline that I was pretty sure was not tummy, so I snagged her as she slunk past and made a closer inspection. Sure enough, two stowaways had somehow managed to get themselves stuffed down inside her dress and were nestling comfortably against her belly button. Conspiracy!

Surprised? Not if you have children, or have spent some time around children. I have three, and all three of them, with monotonous regularity and with premeditated intent, sin against me every day. The dogs don't get fed until the fifth reminder; the note from school gets conveniently lost. The no-shoes-on-the-carpet rule goes unheeded. On and on the list goes. Crimes mount. Charges fill the docket.

Parents, why are we willing to subject ourselves to these abuses day after day? That wasn't in our job descriptions, and we don't have to keep taking it. Let's strike. Why don't we just give up?

I know why I don't give up: because something happens at bedtime.

Nearly every night I tell each of my children goodnight by going into their rooms and making sure that all the important activities are done. We have to get last-minute drinks of water, locate stuffed animals, turn lights off, and offer prayers.

Finally, they fall asleep and that's when it happens. Magically, inexplicably, as I stand gazing upon the small, slumbering reprobates, they transform right before my eyes. They get perfect again and I can't find a single thing wrong with them.

The smudge is still on his face even though we told him three times to wash it off. The Barbie doll is still on the floor, although it belongs in the box. The homework lies as he left it, only half done.

Clearly criminal activity. At least it was a little while ago, but now it doesn't seem so terrible. Now, in the evening's quiet and the muted light from the bathroom door, the smudge and the Barbie doll seem to be only symbols of something. Maybe not even symbols as much as simple reminders.

Reminders of little-boy innocence and carefree childhood security. Reminders of hope for tomorrow, when the room will again come alive with happy songs and little-girl smiles. Reminders that these children are on loan to me for a little while and that, somehow, all the crimes don't make the criminals less perfect.

No, there are no bad people in this room—just children. Something is in my eyes blurring my sight now, but on the other hand, I see perfectly. This new vision fills me with gratitude and clips short the lingering threads of anger and resentment. I offer a quiet prayer of thanks that I am the lucky one who gets to be their Dad.

The homely worm becomes a butterfly. The ugly duckling becomes a swan. The little seed becomes a rare blossom. And my children become perfect. Do you know what I mean?

What causes this miraculous transformation? How can we so easily, even joyfully, offer clemency? Why do our hearts so quickly soften toward these diminutive delinquents?

For me, there are two reasons. First, these children are mine. They belong to me. Second, I love them, and love covers a multitude of sins *(I Peter 4:8)*.

Sound familiar? *Love covers a multitude of sins.* That's not to say that the sin quits happening. It is just not held against the sinner.

It doesn't only work with little girls and kittens. God is like that with me, too, because I am a delinquent son. I go about my day working hard, meeting people, shuffling papers, being a husband, being a Dad, and not doing any of it perfectly. God sees smudges all over my daily record. But at the end of the day, He thinks I am perfect. The record is erased, the criminal is granted clemency and the crimes are forgotten. The blood of Jesus washes them all away.

"But if we live in the light, as God is in the light, we can share fellowship with each other. Then the blood of Jesus, God's Son, cleanses us from every sin" *(I John 1:7)*. The sins don't quit happening just because we walk in the light. We keep committing them, only now we have a new hope for reprieve.

Why? Because He loves us and we are His. Period.

Carter understands the game. She knows without a doubt that her Dad won't hold his anger forever. She delights in the fact that her father is willing—no, eager—to forgive her. That doesn't make her quit her transgressions, though, because she can't. She's just a little girl and kittens are too tempting. She can't live perfectly, but she can live in perfect peace because she knows her Dad, and in his eyes she is perfect. Perfectly adequate to be who she is, perfectly acceptable just as she is, and perfectly welcome in the household. Perfect indeed, because His love has covered a multitude of sins.

"That's the way it is with experience. While you're living it, the importance doesn't impress you. It's only afterward that you can see where it all was leading.**"**

———•◦•———

Stepping Out

A gentle breeze stirred the ashes of the campfire and caressed the sleeping boy's face, disturbing an unruly strand of black hair that had fallen across his cheek. Lost in the carefree, untroubled slumber of youth, the boy didn't stir. The old man half-smiled, remembering.

The man had lived for over a hundred years. How many campfires had he tended? How many miles had he traveled, and how many stories could he tell? Experience, that wisest of teachers, had taught him not to be surprised at anything. But now, at this advanced age, still active in mind and body, the old man found himself on the biggest adventure of his life. In the thousands of years to follow, people would tell over and over again the story that was unfolding at this moment.

But the old man didn't know it. That's the way it is with experience. While you're living it, the importance doesn't impress you. It's only afterward that you can see where it all was leading.

What was it that God had said? "Take now your son, your only son, whom you love, Isaac, and go to the land of Moriah, and offer him there as a burnt offering on one of the mountains" *(Genesis 22:2)*. The old man pondered the directive as the fire slowly died and the stars slid one by one below the horizon. Why? What good could it possibly do? Maybe this was a joke—a little cruel humor from God.

No, it wasn't a joke. The command was real and there was no room for "maybe." What was the old man to do?

What would you do?

"Indian Giver! You promised him to me and now You are taking him back!" Wouldn't you want to strike out, be angry with God? Wouldn't you be tempted to stay in your tent, holding your boy close to you so that nothing, not even God, could take him from you? Isn't blood kin, especially a son of your old age, the most precious gift? Then why was God asking to take him back?

The old man must have contemplated similar questions. The thing was, though, he was already over halfway there. Earlier in the day, curious in his innocence his son had posed a question. "We have fire here, Dad, and wood, but where is the sacrifice?" (author's paraphrase). The old man's answer had been short but clear. "God will provide for Himself the lamb" *(22:8)*.

What was the toughest part of Abraham's journey? Was it when he listened to his son ask the hard questions, knowing that the answers were designed to mislead? Was it along the trail as he watched the excited anticipation in his son's eyes, going on a fun trip with his Dad? Or was it later as he bound his son to the altar, raised his knife to kill him, watching trust turn to bewilderment, then to fear? Where did the journey get hard for Abraham?

It was the first step. When God asks you to do the impossible, it's always the first step that's the killer. There are so many options at this point, so many ways out. "You didn't really mean *me*. Did You?" "It's raining outside. I'll wait until the sun shines." "That was really just a rhetorical suggestion, right?" "I'll need to run this through my committee to make sure this is something that my church wants to do."

Hundreds of arguments. Thousands of obstacles. Only one right step. Sometimes it's a doozy. You have to really, really believe to take that first step. After that, it's a matter of perseverance.

What is God asking you to do? When the adventure is recounted, will it be a big one? Many great stories have never been told because they have never been lived; the star of the show never walked out of his tent. Does God's task scare you, paralyze you with uncertainty? You're at the hard part now. Can you trust God with the outcome—to bring your Isaac back?

Take the first step.

"On that night, Hope went cheap."

———◦•◦———

Hope On The Auction Block

He was a little too drunk going into the curve, so he took it wide and killed Tiffany Bray.

It left a big hole in Magnolia. Cheerleader, member of the student council, volunteer and senior class favorite, she was picked to go places in the world. She got as far as the curve at Spring Creek on Farm to Market Road 2978. The man who killed her died in the same wreck.

The survivors were left to pick up the pieces and try to make sense of it, to redeem some good from the bad, to look for a ray of sunshine in the storm. So they took up a collection, had a fund-raising and promised to give all the money collected to Toys for Tots so little children could have Christmas. It was something good to do in memory of Tiffany.

Hope was a seven-year-old mare, but that wasn't her name until Sandy and Len bought her. Until then she didn't have a name; she was just a dirty white, part-Arabian, head-shy, medium-sized horse. She was at the auction because her owner had brought her with a group of horses hoping to turn a few dollars profit. Hope was just one of the herd he'd brought over; a commodity for trade in pursuit of free enterprise and the American way.

Sandy and Len didn't know Tiffany but they knew God, and they wanted to help with the fund-raising. When the horse came up for bids, they bought her, and that's when she became Hope. On that night, Hope went cheap: six hundred and twenty-five dollars.

Sandy took her home, grain-fed her, combed and trimmed her mane and tail, washed her, cleaned her hooves, trained the shyness out of her, bought a bale of hay, a bag of feed, currycombs and brushes, bridle, saddle, and saddle blanket, and the next week took her back to the auction.

Buster, the stable hand, met them at the gate. "Where'd you get this horse?" he wanted to know.

"It's the same one you rode in the sale arena last week-end, Buster, don't you recognize her?" He didn't, but he did recall an old nag he had ridden that had a scar on her fore-leg just like this one. It couldn't be the same horse, though. This horse was beautiful, glistening white, sleek and healthy, gentle and quiet.

"Folks, I want everybody to listen because we have something special going on tonight with number 12X." The auctioneer talked to his listeners like the friend he was—sincere, straight, and to the point. "This horse was brought here tonight by her owners. The owners have donated 100 percent of the proceeds on this horse to Toys for Tots in honor of Tiffany Bray who was killed down the road here last week. Y'all probably read about her in the newspapers. The owners also have a fund that will match dollar for dollar what the horse brings. If the horse brings fifty dollars, then the fund will match it with another fifty. If the horse brings a thousand dollars, then the fund has to come up with another thousand to match it. You understand? Now who'll bid on this horse in memory of Tiffany? I got five hundred, now six, now seven, eight, now who'll give nine hundred?"

Bids were coming so fast the auctioneer had trouble keeping up. It hung at nine hundred dollars, but then a man standing down front cried out, "Twelve hundred dollars!" Mid-fifties, ostrich boots, Styrofoam cup full of strong drink in his hand, Sandy and Len knew him. He ran a car auction down in Pasadena. Somebody topped it with twelve-fifty and up it went, only to hang again at thirteen hundred. "Who'll give thirteen for this horse?"

"Fifteen hundred!" It was the same man; cowboy hat tilted back, bespectacled face blushing red under the lights. " I want to help those kids. I know these people who are selling this horse. Everything they do they are helping people. I give fifteen hundred."

The crowd was getting into it. Excited talk erupted all around Sandy and Len. Fifteen hundred dollars! Who ever heard of such a thing? Everybody thought that was tops. Nobody would give more than that.

But Hope surprised them.

"Sixteen hundred dollars." It was the couple sitting directly behind Sandy and Len.

"Who'll give sixteen fifty, sixteen fifty, I got sixteen, who'll give sixteen fifty?" the auctioneer chimed in. Nobody would.

"Two thousand dollars!" roared the car salesman. "I want to buy this horse for these kids, but if somebody wants to top me, I won't bid against them."

"Sold for two thousand dollars to bidder number 313. Thank you all!" The place exploded with applause. The auctioneer grinned. The car man gave thumbs up to Len and Sandy, who sat in stunned silence. Hope stood quietly eating her bale of hay.

That night Hope sold high: two thousand dollars; over three times what she had brought last week. What made the difference?

Len and Sandy talked it over on the way home and they figured it out. It was easy, really.

Last week the bidders were just buying horses, but tonight they were buying something else: they were buying Hope, and hope is simply worth a lot more.

"I needed help, somebody to watch my back while I coaxed the old milk cow out of whatever briar patch or sassafras thicket she had gotten herself into."

———•◆•———

A Lot Like Jesus

He was a lot like Jesus. Not that he looked like Him or anything, at least not like the pictures of Jesus I had seen. He was like Him in what he did, or more specifically, what he did that evening a long time ago.

The milking had to be done, but I spent each afternoon wishing it wasn't I who had to do it. Most times I would procrastinate, putting it off until the last minute. By then it was dark and I was too scared to go by myself. The dark holds fearsome images when you are twelve years old, and it could really get dark out there where the only lights were the stars and an occasional firefly. I needed help, somebody to watch my back while I coaxed the old milk cow out of whatever briar patch or sassafras thicket she had gotten herself into.

The most logical choice was Pop, since the chances were mighty slim that one of my brothers would help me. Problem was, Pop was settled in his easy chair by then and it generally took a lot of persuasion to get him out. I tried, anyway.

"Pop, go milk with me." I might as well have been talking to a fence post. I guess he thought I should have gone by myself before it got dark. Of course, I couldn't expect him to understand all the good reasons I hadn't, like playing basketball, eating a jelly sandwich, watching the sunset, and things like that. There was just too much to do before dark, but now I was in a pickle.

He wouldn't go. I tried begging, then nagging, and after an hour or so he got mad at me. He adopted that "I'm -serious -now" sound to his voice and told me to go now or get a busting. I started out of the room but stopped at the door to ask one more time, and that's when the camel's back broke. Here he came, not to help me go milk, but to help me understand with certainty that I should have gone a long time before this.

I was ready to go, now. Yessir, I was on my way, milk bucket in hand, rubber boots slapping my bare legs with every sprinting step. Pop caught up with me halfway across the yard. Even before the first swat landed, I was yelling like a dying man from anticipation of it. Sure enough, it was every bit as bad as I had imagined. He lit into me and commenced to spanking me good. I was squirming this way and that, trying to stay out of harm's way, all the while crying and begging forgiveness, but Pop didn't have it in him right then to demonstrate a forgiving mood.

Now I told you that he was a lot like Jesus. Not Pop; my brother. He hated me, most times. I was usually in his way and I talked too much and said the wrong things and held my head wrong and walked funny and generally embodied everything he didn't like about kids four years younger than he. But he was out there when Pop got me.

I don't recollect how he got there; maybe just evolved from thin air like an angel, or he might have been there all along. He stood about as much of my yelling as he could—probably hurt his ears—and then spoke up, and that's when he got to be like Jesus.

"Pop, please quit whipping Nathan." Pop wasn't listening as he drew back for another swat.

"Whip me, instead."

Well, now...after thirty years of thinking about it, I reckon I love my brother for that. He didn't have to, you know. He wasn't the one in trouble; he had sense enough to go milk on time. I was the guilty one, the one with barnyard dirt on his hands, the one who fully deserved everything Pop was dishing out.

Why did he do that? Don't know for sure, but I can guess: he did it because he wanted to. Maybe he thought I was worth it. He was a lot like Jesus. What a brother.

Don't you wish you had my brother? Somebody to watch your back, somebody willing to be bruised because of your faults, somebody offering to take stripes so that you can be healed *(read Isaiah 53:5)*?

You do.

Jesus.

"Have you ever seen a dirt dauber's house up close? It really isn't a house, after all; it's a nest."

God Made Visible

It would be a lot easier to believe in God if we could see Him, wouldn't it? I mean, it works that way with everything else. When the boss offers you a raise, you believe him more if he actually hands you a paycheck with the promise. When the girlfriend commits to come visit at Thanksgiving, you hold your breath just a little until she actually gets there. It's simply easier to believe in things that we can see and touch. So why would it be any different with God?

I'd like to show God to you, but first listen to this about dirt daubers.

The dirt daubers that live around here are little blue-black bugs that fly. A lot of dirt daubers have died prematurely because they look similar to a stinging wasp. Actually, the creatures are harmless, except to spiders. Their main claim to infamy is that they build their mud homes under the eaves and gutters of houses, sometimes making the owners mad at them.

I got mad at one the other day so I tore his house down. He hadn't bothered asking me for permission, or warned me about it. His house just showed up on my brick wall, so I broke it off.

Have you ever seen a dirt dauber's house up close? It really isn't a house after all; it's a nest. The dirt dauber doesn't live there; it raises its babies there. When I looked at the glob of mud in my hand, I stood in utter amazement.

The little bug had mixed wet dirt and created a hollow tube of dried mud five inches long and half inch in diameter. It reminded me of a drinking straw, except that it was mud. When I broke this straw of dirt off the wall it exposed the inside of the tube, allowing me to see the contents.

The tube was sectioned off into one-inch compartments, and each of the compartments had something in it. The first section held a spider. Until I had messed up the house, this spider had been completely surrounded by a hard wall of dried mud, but he couldn't have gotten away in any case because he was paralyzed. The next compartment held part of a dead spider and a little, wriggling white worm. The third contained a big white grub of a worm that took up nearly the whole space, but there was no evidence of a spider. The next to the last sealed area didn't even have a worm in it, much less a spider. The only thing in the compartment was a motionless, dark brown, hard-shelled, tube-shaped cocoon that was closed on both ends. It looked dead. But the last compartment was the most excellent of all.

I looked in the fifth and what did I see, but a brand new dirt dauber looking up at me. It didn't look anything like a spider, worm or cocoon.

Now who would go to all that trouble? I don't mean the dirt dauber, I mean the designer of the dirt dauber. Who would mastermind a bug so intricately? Who would care enough to create a life that progressed through such precise, complicated stages? Who taught the dirt dauber how to paralyze spiders? How did it know to lay an egg before it sealed off the compartment with the spider in it? Who put the formula together to make such good building material? How did the dirt dauber know that a mud nest was a nearly perfect place to raise young, since predators don't like to eat dirt?

Bugs don't even count. When we think of them at all, we are usually wishing that more of them were dead. So who is this mystery architect that apparently loves dirt daubers?

"The heavens are telling of the glory of God; and their expanse is declaring the work of His hands" shouts the psalmist *(19:1)*. The architect is God, and He's visible through the things He has made. Listen to this: "(God's) invisible attributes, His eternal power and divine nature, have been clearly seen, being understood through what has been made..." That's Romans, first chapter.

Bugs declare the handiwork of God. So, do you want to see God? Look at a dirt dauber. But that's not all.

Have you ever read Psalm 139? It's food for thought. You're like a bug. Before you are anything, you are designed. You are formed in hidden places and your life is ordered. Before you say anything, your architect already knows your thought. You are fearfully and wonderfully made by a master of immense talent.

So, do you want to see God? Look in the mirror.

Each one of you has a job, you know. The dauber's job is to demonstrate the genius of his maker, the eternal power and divine nature of his Creator.

Your job is similar. Know this: people around you—a

lot of them—want to actually see God before they will believe in Him. So what is your task? Simply this: live in such a way that you become God made visible until they are able to know an invisible God.

"Directions to the wedding were simple. Stay on the main highway until you get to Mattie's Ice House, turn into the driveway, park, and walk in."

Preacher At The Ice House

I've heard the whole story from Jerry himself.

Jerry tells how he sat at the kitchen table, scratching his head with one hand and holding a dead phone with the other. In all his years of preaching and tending to people, he had never heard anything to beat this. The call had just come in from a couple who wanted to get married. They couldn't find anybody to do the ceremony on a couple of hours' notice—that is, until they tried Jerry, for he had just hung up from saying yes.

Directions to the wedding were simple. Go on the main highway until you get to Mattie's Ice House, turn into the driveway, park, and walk in. Can't miss it. Even if you don't see the neon sign, you can still tell you're there by the pickup trucks and motorcycles in the parking lot.

Jerry made it over at precisely 2:34 PM—pretty good, considering that they hadn't even called him until 12:30. He had taken the time to shower, give his hair a lick and a promise, grab his marriage sermon book, and kiss his wife goodbye. He was pretty proud of his timing as he pulled into the parking lot. He slid his Buick into a grassy spot beside a machine that could pass for a truck if somebody would give it a good washing and beat it with a sledge hammer for a few hours to get the dents out of it.

Jerry gave one last, appraising glance at his clean-shaven face in the rearview mirror, allowed himself a half-grin at what he and God had gotten themselves into, got out of the car and walked confidently smack into the world of redneck Bubbas and longneck beers.

Cheap perfume, cigarette smoke, and spilled beer welcomed his nose at the door while his eyes roamed about searching for the blissful pair. What used to be a pretty good buck deer stared down from its place on the wall with benevolent, watchful care, its antlers adorned with assorted caps and bead necklaces. Some considerate soul had placed a fine cigar in its mouth, unlit of course, but the deer didn't care.

Jerry spotted a little group of people over in the corner and figured he had found them. Sure enough, the bride-to-be was sitting on her intended's lap there at the little wooden table, although she could have pulled up a chair of her own if she'd wanted to. She was a cute brunette, and although Jerry thought she overdid it a little with the cheap jewelry and makeup, he was singularly impressed when she stood up, met his gaze, and shook his hand in a straightforward, honest way of greeting him.

The groom-to-be looked up through a cloud of cigarette smoke and grinned at Jerry. He was well put together, with big, heavily muscled arms sticking out the short sleeves of his Harley Davidson™ T-shirt. Scuffed cowboy boots tapped the rhythm of a country song playing quietly from the jukebox. Jerry figured they had it turned down in honor of the occasion.

Everybody at the table introduced themselves and somebody offered Jerry a drink, then got embarrassed when the groom smacked him on the back of the head and reminded him that Jerry was a preacher. Formalities over, Jerry got down to business.

He stood in front of the little crowd, and somehow the noise in the background quieted down enough so that

Jerry didn't even need to raise his voice very much.

"Do you, Imogene Biggs, take this man to be your lawfully wedded husband, to have and to hold ..." Jerry knew it all by heart, but still glanced down at the book from time to time through force of habit. The bride stood with chin up, back stiff and eyes bright as she listened carefully to Jerry going through the speech. At that moment they could have been anywhere—a château in France, a glistening beach in Hawaii, or a cruise ship in the middle of the Caribbean. Her serious expression and obvious awareness of the gravity of the statement she was about to make lent her a calm poise and dignity that elevated the ceremony up and out of the ice house, way on up there where the air was pure and the sun bright, so high that you thought you were right up close to heaven. This was the union of two hearts, the promise of a lifetime, 'till-death-do-us-part kind of commitment, and she was willing to do it. She was standing beside her man and she wanted everybody in the world to know it.

"Well, then, you may kiss the bride." It was over and everybody in the place clapped as the groom scooped his new wife up into his arms, lifting her off the floor like a baby, and kissed her full on the mouth. Jerry laughed out loud and marveled at God for being smart enough to make marriages.

When things quieted down, Jerry gathered the new couple and all their friends in a circle and invited them to pray the Lord's Prayer with him. This was new for some of them and they didn't know what to do with their beers. "What about cigarettes? Do you reckon the Big Guy cares if a fellow has a little smoke?" somebody whispered.

"Better put it out for this one," someone else whispered in reply. The circle grew larger as more people joined in, and they all started to lock arms or hold hands as they stood there.

"Our Father Who art in Heaven, Hallowed be Thy Name." After Jerry spoke the first few words, another voice joined in, and then another. By the time they got to "Forgive us our trespasses," everybody in the room was there, saying it strong, clear and loud, no shame or embarrassment, just talking to God while the deer looked down on them, approving.

"For Thine is the Kingdom and the power and the glory forever. Amen." Jerry looked up to see heads still bowed. Tears were streaming down the faces of two or three and sober realization was apparent on others. They slowly unlocked arms and quietly visited among themselves for a while longer. One or two came up to Jerry and told him what a fine job he had done.

One man, in particular, was still crying softly. He told Jerry that his Momma had been praying for him a long time, and that maybe it was time he changed his ways. Jerry grinned at him and his eyes sparkled. Jerry said, "God probably brought you here today just so you would be in a place where you were comfortable enough to listen to what God had to say." The man looked startled; then he admitted Jerry was probably right.

I reckon they still talk about it up at Mattie's—the day God came to the ice house. Jerry reflects on it from time to time, sometimes laughing out loud at the memory, at the humor of God to take him to a place like that.

And I hear that people still go to the ice house and that the customers still dance to the country music pouring from the jukebox. The deer still presides over the drinking place, although somebody eventually stole its cigar and smoked it themselves.

But not everybody goes who used to. You see, I was there when Jerry and God walked in that day. I've always thought they came because of Momma. The way I've got it figured, Momma prayed so much about it that she nearly wore God out, so He brought Jerry in on it to bring God into the only place I would listen to Him: the ice house.

I might be wrong about why they came, but it doesn't matter. What matters, and what has made all the difference, is that when they left, God took me with Him.

"The first words I remember him saying were "Gee" and "Haw," not to me but to Burt the white mule as the two plowed the garden together."

———•◦•———

Still Never Leaving

"Hey, what are you doing in that chair? Get up and let's go feed the chickens," Luther said to Veeje, but he knew she wasn't going to get up.

Luther was nearly sixty when I was born, and had already put in a lifetime of hard work before I could walk. The first words I remember him saying were "Gee" and "Haw," not to me but to Burt the white mule as the two plowed the garden together. Every spring of my young life those words rang clear through the cool air and across the draw that separated our houses.

Veeje was with him the whole time. I didn't know how many years they had been sweethearts, but I knew it had been a long time, because when she didn't get up from her chair, he wasn't mad at her. He didn't expect her to get up because the stroke had paralyzed her.

Luther and Veeje exchanged grins, his loose and easy, hers slow and labored. Luther took a bowl of sauce over to his wife's chair and spoon-fed her, sitting by her side, bantering with her like a teenager on a date. By this time, they were both over eighty.

Veeje knew with a deep understanding what she meant to Luther. When he had told her that he wouldn't leave until one of them died, she believed him. When they had moved on to their Tennessee farm at a time when families were living in their barns until their houses were built, he stayed with her. When they journeyed through their hard-working years, he was there. When she lost her youthful vigor and appearance, he stayed. When the stroke took her health and reduced her to what some people would call a useless, wasted human, Luther didn't realize it; he thought she was still his bride. And now here he was, flirting with her, still her main man, and still never leaving.

What is that worth? Would you give one million dollars for it, if you had a million dollars? What value would you place on someone who promised to never leave, and then kept his promise? For Veeje, it was worth everything she had, and she proved it by giving her life to Luther. She knew what a treasure he was.

You and I need a Luther. We need someone who won't leave. We can't have Luther, because he is Veeje's, but we need someone. Have you experienced the dread of abandonment, the soul-breaking pain of infidelity, the grief of death? People leave, even the best of them. It's all temporary. What would it be worth to you to have someone who is permanent?

Jesus knows what it is worth. For Him, it is worth everything. He proved it by giving His life, not because He needed to, but because you needed Him to.

"I will never desert you, nor will I ever forsake you" *(Hebrews 13:5)*. "I am with you always, even to the end of the age" *(Matthew 28:20)*. Jesus is the speaker and you are the audience. The words are real and so is the promise.

And there He is, still. Still present. Still available. Still never leaving.

What is that worth?

"The toy mower had a noise-maker in it that made noise as long as the mower was moving. He kept it moving, being careful not to "kill" the engine."

———•••———

Toy Tools

I caught a flash of color out of the corner of my eye, so I turned to look. A red and yellow plastic lawnmower moved with great purpose through the freshly cut grass behind me. Attached to the mower was a two-year-old boy, strutting with self-importance, taking big steps, keeping up. He was on the job, cutting the grass with his Dad.

How precious is that? I paused, watched, and laughed. His tennis shoes were untied and stained green, and he ran this way and that, trying not to miss any grass. The toy mower had a noisemaker in it that made noise as long as the mower was moving. He kept it moving, being careful not to "kill" the engine.

I left my mower—the one that actually cut grass—and walked over to him. He didn't see me coming and I was nearly on top of him before he looked up, startled. He had seen Dad walk toward him before, with mixed results, and he didn't know how this would end up. He was trying hard, but maybe he had missed some spots and I wouldn't like it. He stopped his mower and hung his head.

I had to stoop to look him in the eye. "Logan, you sure are doing a good job, boy. Look at all that grass you cut. I'm really proud of you." The head came up, his eyes brightened, and he smiled all over his face. He had passed. His Dad approved.

Approval. It has tremendous power, and in some relationships it can be earned with toy tools.

Take another look at the child. Tongue sticking out of the corner of his mouth, feet working fast, both hands on the handlebars, brow knit with concentration. Busy.

Doing what?

Nothing much. He wasn't cutting grass because his mower was plastic. He wasn't earning his keep; he was just two years old. He wasn't helping because his tools were toys. Besides, I didn't need any help. Well, what was he doing, then, that made me so happy?

Just one thing. He was trying to be like me.

The job he was doing wasn't the thing. The delight I felt, the warmth in my heart toward him, the treasure I keep in my memory was the little boy's sincere, genuine and totally unpretentious effort to imitate me. I didn't care if he wasn't really cutting grass, because he was doing all a two-year-old could do, and that was enough.

Now, how old are you in God's eyes? Maybe you think you have outgrown the toy stage. Your tools are bigger and much more important, and they don't have toy-sounding names. Your tools are called Responsibility. Authority. Accountability. Money. These are all big and powerful tools for doing great service to God, right?

How much good are you doing?

Maybe our tools are toys. I suspect they are. Our work doesn't carry the weight that we wish it did. We are purposeful, busy, and on the job. We want to do great things for God, but maybe we aren't doing it right. Perhaps we don't get the right opportunity, or getting it, we mess it up somehow by being too weak, or too ignorant, or by having the wrong personality. Or, more often, we don't really even know if what we are doing is what God wants. And, unlike a two-year-old, we are acutely aware of it. How could God possibly approve of us?

Let's go back in time to a place called Jerusalem. There,

a man wanted to build something for God—a house, to be exact. King David spent years at the drafting table formulating plans, arranging materials, laying the groundwork. Busy. On the job. Doing something great for God.

God didn't need a house because He doesn't dwell in houses. David couldn't help God; God didn't need any help. David had a strong desire, but his tools weren't adequate to be worthy of the Almighty and his house wasn't big enough to contain Him.

What did God think about that? Did He laugh at the idea? Did He ridicule David for his childish project and urge him to give up his silly dream for a real job?

No. He wouldn't let David build the house, but listen to what He told David: "Because it was in your heart to build a house for My name, you did well that it was in your heart" (II Chronicles 6:8).

Approval. What a message!

Toy tools. Mine aren't much to look at and I'm not a very good expert for God. I want to do great things for God, but my tools aren't adequate, and I can't be as productive as I would like. About all I can do is run around with my plastic lawnmower, getting my tennis shoes green, trying my best to be like Him.

What does God think of me? Well, if the story of

King David is any indication, I imagine God smiles at my efforts, at my grass-stained footwear, my purposeful strides and close-knit brow, and that His response is gentle with approval.

"Nathan, you can't do that job. But, because it was in your heart to do it, you did well."

"What is freedom, anyway? It has to do with multiple choice."

Coyote Freedom

It was for freedom that Christ set us free." Now, there's a phrase.

I had been focusing on a bran muffin this morning, but now it lay by the coffee cup, barely touched, because I was reading Galatians, fascinated by the message. There it was, fifth chapter, first verse: "For it was for freedom that Christ set us free." Now why would Paul say something like that? This was an enigma. On the surface it seemed to be redundant, because why else would you be set free except to be set free? It appeared obvious.

But when I take a closer look, I begin to understand that it's not that simple. Sometimes, being set free has strings attached. Take the rodeo, for example. One event involves putting a calf into a pen barely big enough to hold it, and then turning it loose—setting it free, so to speak. Why? To get caught again. That's the object.

Here's another example: the honey industry. Beekeepers catch a wild bee, tie a string to its leg and turn it loose. Why? Because it will fly back to its home and the beekeeper then will be able to capture the whole hive. Being set free is not always for the purpose of freedom. Sometimes it is for the purpose of being enslaved again.

What does it mean, then, to be set free for freedom's sake?

Marty Stouffer makes wildlife movies. His specialty is filming wild animals as they meet and interact with one another, typically on a hunter/hunted basis. I once watched one of his films in which a coyote was chasing a jackrabbit. Both participants were out in a meadow with plenty of room to run. The jackrabbit was magnificent. He seemed to defy gravity as he executed incredible zigzags and broad jumps.

The coyote was nearly as quick. He had a little more inertia to deal with than the rabbit since there was more of him to get into motion, but he was doing fine. At one point during the chase Marty zoomed in for a close-up of the coyote's face, and I must say, I believe the animal was grinning. He looked like he was having the time of his life.

Let's say I'm right. Let's suppose the coyote really was happy. If he was, then he is a perfect example of the freedom Paul is talking about.

Watch the coyote. Eyes squinted against the wind, tongue hanging out, ears laid back, tail whipping for balance, smiling at the chase. Loving it. But what is he actually doing? What is the coyote trying to accomplish?

He's trying to make a living. He is on the job. Think about it. The coyote must catch that rabbit or one like it because his life depends on it. It just happens that in this case he *loves* to do what he *must* do.

What is freedom, anyway? It has to do with multiple choice. It's the option to choose. Is the coyote free? It depends upon which area of his life we are talking about. He is not free from his appetite, so in a sense he is a slave. He is a slave to his hunger. If he is a slave, though, then why is he grinning? Because he loves to do what he has to do in order to satisfy his appetite. So, in a sense he is free. Consider this: if you were a slave and you loved it, then you wouldn't be a slave at all. You would be free. Why? Because you would be doing slave duty by choice. Why do we crave freedom in the first place, if not for the option it gives us to do what we love to do?

It was for freedom that Christ set us free. Sometimes freedom involves doing the things that are required of a servant, but doing them by choice, and with joy. We are all servants of something. We don't have a choice in this matter. We can't choose not to be a servant, but we can do something better than that. We can choose whose servant we will be.

Some masters will set us free for a while, only to capture us again in the end. Money will do that. Sexual freedom will do it. A hunger for power will accomplish the same thing, as will mood-altering drugs, and even food.

The Good Shepherd will set us free and we will never again have to fear being captured, because it was for the sake of freedom that He set us free. So now we can go about our days with joy, grinning like a coyote chasing a jackrabbit, working our jobs, tending to our responsibilities, doing the boring tasks along with the fun ones, tackling the hard problems as enthusiastically as the easy ones. We can do this, knowing that it is the Lord Christ we are serving, and that to be His servant is not at all burdensome *(Matthew 11:30)*, but is freedom indeed.

"Where did we get the idea that what we see is all there is?"

See A Little Better

A newborn day was painting the western hills pink when a young man woke up, looked about—and thought he would die *(read II Kings 6:15)*.

How did he get into this mess, anyway? If it weren't for that crazy man, Elisha, he wouldn't even be here. Elisha flatly refused to act normal. Everything he did was radical, and he didn't care who got mad at him.

Elisha was a great man of God, but he had a bad temper. For one thing, he was touchy about his hairdo. "Go up, thou bald head" *(II Kings 2)*. The children who poked fun at him paid with their lives. Elisha called a bear out of the woods to kill seventeen of them. He was a strange individual, Elisha.

But he had overdone it this time—thwarted the wrong man—got the king of Syria mad at him, and now the whole Syrian army was here, surrounding the city, looking for one man: Elisha. Which was fine except for one thing: the young man was with Elisha and when they got Elisha, they would kill him, too.

Now, how do you handle it when the odds are forty thousand to two? You might be tempted to do what the young man did: Look at what you see, consider what is likely to happen based upon the evidence—and promptly despair.

But hold on a second. Where did we get the idea that what we see is all there is? That surely can't be true. Just consider air; you can't see it, but you know it is there. And what about radio waves, x-rays, thoughts, electricity, and heat? You could fill a room full of these and then take a photo of them, but the pictures would show an empty room. Some of the most real things in the world aren't apparent to those who can't see.

So it was with the young man. He was terror-stricken because he looked at the available evidence and reached a conclusion based upon what he saw. Does it surprise you that he was wrong?

"But I'm a realist, and I must consider the evidence", you might say. "What I can actually see with my own eyes are more wrinkles in the mirror, elevated corruption in the government, a late mortgage bill on my kitchen table, and a report card full of failing grades in my 8th grader's back-pack". Perhaps it is all true, but what is your conclusion? Despair? Let's take another look at Elisha.

Two men looked at the same situation but what they saw was dramatically different. The servant perceived gloom and destruction, but Elisha envisioned total, absolute, utter victory. The reason? Better eyes. When we can really see, things look better.

The disciples thought a ghost was coming on the waters, and they were frozen in fear. But when they saw that it was Jesus, Peter came out to meet Him *(read Matthew 14:26)*. Thomas doubted until he saw; then he proclaimed, "My Lord and my God *(John 20:28)*". The Ethiopian eunuch was confused and without direction. Philip helped him see, and he went on his way rejoicing *(Acts 8:39)*. What a marvelous gift, sight.

Elisha's servant needed help because he was missing some important parts. All he could see was the enemy army and he needed to know about the friendly forces that were on his side. The mountains were crowded with horses and chariots of God, far more powerful than those against him were. That's how Elisha put it: "Those who are with us are more than those who are with them *(II Kings 6:16).*" Notice that the friendly troops didn't arrive just so the young man could see them; they were present all along. The lad didn't feel better until he saw them, but he was just as safe.

I believe that God can show Himself or his helpers to us anytime He wants, but we will suffer needless pain if we insist upon it. Most of the time we are left to handle the struggle without direct knowledge of help, and that is well pleasing to Him. The doubting Thomas believed when he saw, but Jesus told him a better way: "Blessed are they who did not see, and yet believed *(John 20:29).*"

I can really relate to Elisha's servant. On my desk as I write is a list of fourteen projects that I think are essential yet appear impossible. The odds are too great against me; the enemy warhorses are snorting fire and it seems like they are charging at me. I'm tempted to despair, give up in defeat before the battle starts, because it looks too hard.

But hold on a second. What makes me think that what I perceive is all there is? Maybe if I could see a little better . . . .

"I saw the whole thing. The wagon hit the hole and Pop rolled off in front of it. I saw him hit the ground and then I didn't see him any-more."

———•◆•———

Hay And Grace

Hold on, Pop, hold on!" I was screaming with pure terror. My father was going to die, and it was my fault.

We were on the last load of hay out of the field. Tired, a long way from the barn, with dark coming on, I wanted to take the shortcut. The shortcut saved time, but it led down a hill. If I took the long way, it was level. I was the driver.

Nineteen years old, rawhide-tough, bull-strong, bulletproof and dumb, I forgot about the simple laws of physics. If you are going down a hill pulling a load of hay, and the hay weighs more than the tractor, then the hay will tend to push the tractor down the hill at the same rate of speed that the hay would have gone down on its own, which is way too fast.

I forgot, so I started down the hill pulling a hundred and thirty bales of hay, with my father riding on the front lip of the wagon between the tractor and the hay.

The first I knew of trouble was when the brake wouldn't work. I pressed it, and the wheels locked up, but the tractor didn't slow down. In fact, it was going faster and faster, with the weight of the hay wagon pushing it. I glanced behind me and I knew with sick realization that if we hit a bump, my father would fall off the wagon and the whole load of hay would roll over him. If that happened, there was simply no way he would survive.

We were going too fast. The load was completely out of control. Near the bottom of the hill, the tractor hit a huge hole in the ground. The front dropped, then flew into the air as the back wheels hit the hole. Then the back of the tractor left the hole, bucking like a half-broken-in mule, and it was the wagon's turn.

I saw the whole thing. The wagon hit the hole and Pop rolled off in front of it. I saw him hit the ground and then I didn't see him anymore.

Hay was everywhere, all over the ground. The tractor and wagon were stopped; I didn't know how. I knew my father was dead. I had seen him fall off in front of the wagon.

I had to find him.

It was dark, and piles of hay littered the ground. The wagon lay where it had stopped, canted to one side with its tongue buried deep into the ground. I was in a daze, yelling over and over, "Where's my Dad, where's my Dad?"

I had been dog-tired, but now the heavy bales of hay seemed to almost lift themselves of their own accord and fling themselves aside as I desperately searched for my father. I couldn't find him. I was crying.

"I'm here. Get the hay off me." I heard faint words over my sobbing, so I threw the hay away from the sounds and there was my father, lying on the ground, scratched up but otherwise healthy. And most important—not dead.

How did that happen? Well, it was a simple law of physics. When the tractor hit the hole, the wagon tongue broke loose from the tractor and buried itself in the ground, stopping the wagon. My father ended up four feet in front of the front wheel of the wagon. When the wagon stopped so suddenly, the hay kept moving and spilled off down the front of the wagon, covering up my Dad.

Well, that's how it happened, and it makes a good story, but I don't like to think about it, about my ignorance and irresponsibility. I don't like to think about what almost happened.

But I do want to know the "why." Why did I get a reprieve? Why was it that, fully deserving the bitter consequences of my poor decision, I was granted the grace to live without bearing the burden of having killed my father?

It was grace. Now I know that physics was involved, and physics can tell me how it happened, but only grace can explain why. I really don't know why, so I can only guess at some possibilities.

Maybe God knew that I could not have survived the pain of knowing that I had killed my father, so He was saving me from an early death. Maybe Pop still had some of the Father's work to do and he was too valuable here to be taken away by the whim of a teenager. Or, maybe I needed to have the chance to make more mistakes without this one destroying me, so that I could grow up to be a useful tool for the Savior. I really don't know....I just don't know.

Hay and grace. I learned a lot about both that hot June evening.

Hay is dangerous. It can kill you. You need to exercise wisdom in the handling of it.

Grace is powerful, amazingly powerful, and in the hands of the Savior it can preserve lives and transform people. I think I'm living proof because there on a hillside farm in a dark Tennessee meadow, I believe the hand of God had reached out and touched a young boy in trouble, changing his life and keeping it whole.

His grace had reached even me.

"Here is something I believe about a dog. A dog thinks that if he is not getting killed right now, he will live forever."

Dogs And Forever

A ground-shaking bawl started somewhere in his tail and came rolling down off his tongue like a bell, loud and clear. Leaves trembled on the ghost-white sycamores, scattering moonlight across the creek waters. The old hunter sitting beside the fire was thrilled and the critters of the night felt a chill. A familiar and dreaded note hung on the evening air—the lonesome melody of an old-time hunting hound singing his ancient tune.

He was on a hot trail. There had been no coon tracks down on the water, so the flop-eared hunter had left the creek and run to the ridge searching for new ground. There he stopped cold, nose to the ground, leg muscles quivering.

A new scent was on the ground. Untold generations of hunting ancestry set up a clamoring in his nose, driving him to a frenzy, urging him on to follow this strange, new track.

Now he was gaining on the prey, his hound dog bawls ringing through the hills and his pounding feet revealing his eagerness to finish the race as winner.

Suddenly, there was his quarry, crouched where it had stopped on the far side of an old log, lips curled in a snarl, fangs bared to his pursuer, spring-steel muscles taut with fury.

Nobody had told the dog about bobcats. Roaring with triumph, he closed in on the cat, doing what finely tuned hunting dogs do: going for the kill.

Seconds later, the fight was over, not because either animal got killed, but because the dog got whipped. His brute strength was no match for the lightning agility and razor-like claws of the cat. It had raked him three times before he could pounce, leaving bloody gashes across his face and head.

Howls of charging victory turned to whimpers of tail-tucking retreat. Terror stuck in his throat, fear of death lent wings to his legs, and realization of imminent annihilation moved him to abandon the field, conceding defeat at the hands of the annoyed feline.

Minutes later, back at the campfire and close to his

master, the dog flopped down beside the blaze, thumped his tail a couple of times, and dozed off to sleep.

No ulcers. No tranquilizers to help him sleep. No counseling sessions for post-traumatic stress syndrome. None of that. Just simple, sit-by-the-fire type serenity.

What's wrong with that dog?

He must have some kind of problem. Why isn't he shaking, reliving the horrible encounter in his mind, processing his narrow escape? Doesn't he know that he nearly got killed a few minutes earlier? How can he relax so quickly?

I think I know. It's because he is a dog.

Here is something I believe about a dog. A dog thinks that if he is not getting killed right now, he will live forever, and that is why he doesn't worry. He doesn't worry about what happened in the past; it didn't kill him. And, he doesn't worry about what might happen in the future; it hasn't happened yet. A dog, I believe, lives in the moment. Everything is a perpetual "now."

Therein lies the difference between a dog and a man.

A human isn't like a dog because a human can get scared and worried about things that don't have anything to do with now. A snake bit you when you were five years old. Thirty years later you are still afraid to walk in the weeds. The preacher insulted us in public when we were thirteen.

That preacher is long since dead, but we still hate preachers. Late one evening a group of friends jumped out from behind a tree at me and a lifetime later, I am still scared of the dark.

Unlike dogs, we humans spend a lot of time in the past, processing dumb mistakes, shameful activities, lost opportunities. Then we immediately start worrying about the future, thinking that we will do the same things again.

Where do we make room for "now"?

If we really could live at this moment in our minds, never thinking about the past or future, we wouldn't have many worries. We would be like that dog, but we don't really want to be like a dog. Dogs might not worry about the future, but they probably don't hope for the future either, and we want to be able to hope for the future. Dogs don't regret the past, but they might not have sweet memories of it either, and we want to have sweet memories. We want to be able to think across time—both ways—but not suffer the negatives that this ability seems to foster.

Who can help us?

"Come to Me, all who are weary and heavy-laden, and I will give you rest" *(Matthew 11:28)*. The words belong to Jesus. The promise is real. I think he is talking to me.

How can Jesus help?

He controls the future and forgives the past, making me free to live now. Listen to these scriptures: "Why are you worried about clothing? Observe how the lilies of the field grow; they do not toil . . . yet I say to you that not even Solomon in all his glory clothed himself like one of these" *(Matthew 6:28)*. "Are not two sparrows sold for a cent? And yet not one of them will fall to the ground apart from your Father...So do not fear; you are more valuable than many sparrows" *(Matthew 10:29, 31)*. "Let us not lose heart in doing good, for in due time we will reap if we do not grow weary" *(Galatians 6:9)*.

Let's revisit our injured dog.

Where is he now? Lying by the fire, at the feet of his master. Where did he run in his hour of need? His master. Who lends him comfort and security against cats that kill? His master. The dog has an inborn knowledge that he needs to be with his master when he is in trouble.

Same with me. When I'm in trouble now, or regretting being in trouble in the past, or worried about being in trouble in the future, I need to go to the feet of my Master. My fears might not be based upon reality, but the fears themselves are real, so I need some relief. I might be regretting something that, in truth, was not my fault, but the regret itself feels the same as if it really was my fault. I need help for my feelings, because they are real, even if the events that caused the feelings are not.

The feet of Jesus. I can go there when I am gashed and bloody from the fight. I can go there when I am worn out from the struggle, when courage has fled and hope seems a mockery. He will protect me from the dangers of the dark forest because I am more valuable than flowers and birds. With Him I can recapture my ability to live "*now*," to be relieved of the burdens of yesterday and to be free from the worry of tomorrow.

Like a dog, you and I need a Master, one with power over regrets and worries. One who controls the past, present, and future. Someone eternal.

Someone like Jesus.

"The greatest mental health problem of humans is loneliness."

———•◆•———

I'm On Your Side

They said "I do" when they were nineteen, then at forty-five she said, "I don't anymore," and walked off. The damage was considerable.

Whose fault was it? You don't know because there are too many facts to sort out, even if you could get the facts.

Maybe it just happened. Perhaps they were victims of the "creeping separateness" syndrome that plagues so many couples. Not active hostility, just a lack of effort eroding the relationship and leaving nothing but a pit of half-forgotten promises and washed-out dreams. In this case, the pit was unbearable, so she climbed out.

He comes a thousand miles to sit on your porch and

get answers. What do you say?

The questions are too hard.

What words will help with twenty-six years of memories haunting him, reminding him of all the things he should have done differently, and would have, if he had only seen it more clearly? What will heal the memories?

There are supposed to be answers for these problems, aren't there? Surely, if you are smart enough and have gone to enough classes and read the right books, you can find the right words.

So I try my best. Sitting with him on the porch in the cool of the evening, steaming cups of coffee in our hands, I give it all I have.

"I'm sure sorry this happened to you and I want you to know that I'm on your side." That's it. I don't know what else to say.

It wasn't a very rich reward for a thousand-mile effort. At least I didn't think so.

He thought differently. A slow smile started on his face and quickly grew to a wide grin. "Well, thank you, Bro."

I'm on your side. What a statement. Jess Lair wrote a book called "*I Ain't Well but I Sure Am Better.*" In it, he said that the greatest mental health problem of humans is loneliness. He thinks we need two or three people in our lives who really know us but still like us. These are people whose faces light up when we walk into the room just because we are who we are, not because of what we possess or what we have done. We're talking here of people who don't care which side of the argument we are on—they just know that they are on our side.

Am I wrong for being on his side? Isn't it irresponsible of me to do that when I don't know whose fault it was? Maybe it was all his doing. What if the smoking gun points to him? Perhaps his fingerprints are all over the scene of the crime.

Maybe I'm mistaken but, really, who cares whose fault it is? What does it matter? We aren't judging here; he has already been judged, convicted and sentenced, and now he is doing time in his own mind, so he doesn't need any of that from me.

Do you think God will get mad at us if we align ourselves with guilty people? Let's take a look at Jesus.

"She's caught in adultery, and our law says kill her. What do You say?" *(see John 8:4-5)*

Who will plead her case? When the accusers leave, she and Jesus are the only ones there. "Where are those who condemned you?" They are conspicuously absent. "I do not condemn you either" *(8:11). I'm on your side.*

Was she guilty? You bet. He didn't care.

The word is out that He eats with tax collectors and sinners. Zaccheus is the chief tax collector, but right now he is up in a tree because he wants to see Jesus. Instead, Jesus sees him. "Zaccheus, hurry and come down, for today I must stay at your house" *(Luke 19:5)*. *I'm on your side.*

How many people had Zaccheus cheated? We don't know, and Jesus didn't care.

Hanging on each side of Him were two thieves, but one said, "Remember me..." Jesus replied, "...Today you will be with me in paradise" *(Luke 23:43)*. *I'm on your side.*

The crook beside the innocent, asking for a favor. He gets it.

"I'm on your side." Do you know who needs to hear that more than anyone else? The guilty.

It's easy to be on the side of the saint. He has the glory, the virtue and all the things we admire. But how many saints do you know? Most of us don't run in saintly circles; we are among the common folk who sin and have character flaws and are generally not beautiful humans. What do these, the guilty people need? They need room to get better, and the only thing that will allow it is for someone to be on their side.

Thank God for Jesus, who, although perfect, nevertheless took the side of the guilty and gave us room to get better. If I'm correct, He died for the ungodly. That would be me.

So, today, I'd like to pass that on: I am on your side.

"What could happen to a man that would make him suddenly switch from stealing a shirt to shedding a tear?"

————•◦•————

Severe Mercy

Three hotdogs for a dollar was the bait that lured me into the convenience store. I had it all planned out. The juvenile probation department was paying me a regular wage, but I didn't want to spend all my money on food, so I was hunting a cheap lunch. Along with the hotdogs I could get a twenty-five-cent moon pie and a fifty-cent drink. Cheap enough. I wheeled in.

The moon pies were at the rear of the store, and while I was back there, a man walked in. He had shaggy hair, a black beard and mustache, old tennis shoes, worn-out jeans, and a faded shirt. I glanced out the window to see a beat-up car with a woman and some scraggly kids in it, obviously all his.

The store had T-shirts for sale on a rack next to me, and while I pondered the virtues of chocolate versus vanilla moon pies, the man walked back to the rack and looked through the shirts. One caught his eye so he pulled it from the hanger and held it up. Satisfied with his selection, the man wadded the shirt up and stuck it down in his pants. When he was done you couldn't tell it was there.

I just stood there. Now what? I was starting to wish I had skipped the moon pie. What should I do? I listed some options in my mind.

The simplest thing to do would be to ignore it. It wasn't my business, literally. The store could probably afford the loss of a three-dollar shirt. After all, shoplifting was a fact of life for convenience stores.

Another option was to tell the clerk. I knew the clerk. She was nineteen years old. I doubted that she would know what to do.

Or, I could make a citizen's arrest. I did a quick mental comparison and decided that I could probably take the fellow in a brawl if need be. But there was always the chance that he wouldn't appreciate the citizen's arrest, and then I would have to try to deal with the brawl issue.

Frankly, I didn't know what to do. I thought that I *ought* to know what to do, but I still didn't know. None of the choices held any appeal. I was beginning to hate hot-dogs and convenience stores and being put in this position. Mostly, I was hating myself for being too dumb to know how to handle this situation.

Worst of all, the man was directly behind me in line. While I had been considering my dilemma, I was busy squirting mustard on my three hot-dogs and icing down my drink at the fountain. Now I was paying the clerk, and the man with the stolen shirt was directly behind me. He had a cold drink in his hand, but the shirt was nowhere in sight.

I was running out of time. I got my change and opened the door to leave.

"You want me to buy that shirt for you?"

Who said that? The words had come from me and I was already regretting them. Ingram, what in the world have you done, sticking your nose in business where you don't belong? You've struck a match to a powder keg and now it's going to blow up.

The question stunned the man. He just looked at me. He tried to bluff it out, acting like the question didn't apply to him.

"Huh?" He wasn't very verbal.

"I'll buy that shirt for you if you want me to."

"What shirt?"

I wanted him to shut up. I didn't want to talk to him. I just wanted him to let me buy the shirt for him so I could get out of there. What was I doing talking to him in the first place, anyway?

"Well, I hated to see you leave without paying for it, so I'll buy it for you if you'll let me."

He was caught, red-handed and red-faced. He pulled the shirt from his pants. "No, I'll put it back. I'm sorry." This was directed to the nineteen-year-old clerk who had been looking on in speechless wonder.

I thought about the scraggly kids outside. "No, really. If you don't mind, I'll buy it for you."

"Who are you?"

"I'm Nathan, and I'll buy that shirt if you'll let me."

"Are you a Christian?"

Now what kind of question was that? I was embarrassed. In the first place, I didn't even know what I was doing, and secondly, I was pretty sure that I was messing up so badly that Jesus wouldn't want to have His name attached to mine. Jesus would have known exactly how to act and what to say, but I didn't.

"I'm just trying to be. Can I buy the shirt?" Since he had brought Jesus up, maybe I could tell him what Jesus did for him. At the least, I should be able to deliver a mini-lecture on the evils of theft and the fear of judgment. I couldn't think. All I could do was to keep on offering to buy the dumb shirt, desperately hoping he would let me so I could leave.

He didn't. He started crying. Not that loud, sobbing-type of crying. Not even screw-your-face-up crying. Just the eye-filling, voice-stealing kind that comes out of a full-grown man not used to doing it.

"Man, I've never seen anybody like you." Neither had I. Anybody else would have done a lot better. He apologized again, this time to me and the clerk.

I got my hotdogs, the clerk got her money, and the man got his shirt. Then he left with his wife, kids, and beat-up car. I haven't seen him since.

I have a question. What made him cry? What could happen to a man to make him suddenly switch from stealing a shirt to shedding a tear? I think I know, because that man and I are a lot alike.

You see, I know about doing wrong, and not necessarily worrying about how it affects anybody else. So does he. I have had to face the reality of my depravity in a shame-torn circumstance of my own creation, without a whisper of an excuse to help my case. So has he. Then, when all the evidence justified my condemnation, I have had Jesus offer me His grace to help in my time of need. And I have been touched to the core with wonder, and awed in the presence of something good without appropriate expression for it except the unspoken language of tears. His offer to help me brings more reproach than a hundred lashes, and no response is necessary except, "I'm sorry."

We are much alike, that man and I. We have both received a severe mercy.

"Sure enough, not five feet from his window perched a mockingbird—six ounces of pure music wrapped up in a bunch of feathers...."

Singing In The Dark

Tommy jumped and landed upright in bed, throwing the covers clear and looking wildly around. Printed blue pajamas covered his racing heart, and terror made him pant like a sprinter. A bear had been chasing him and had finally run him over a cliff, but instead of crashing to the rocks below, he had landed in his bedroom, on his own bed, with no bear in sight. Not sure whether it had been a dream, the child sat still as a statue, listening hard into the night for the slightest sound.

Stars, brilliant in the darkness, let a soft glow into the bedroom, and the open window filtered the muted tones of a countryside springtime night. The sound of each rustling leaf and singing cricket magnified the boy's fear. His imagination peopled the backyard with horrible monsters that had dripping fangs and appetites that craved little children.

A stirring of the leaves in the apple tree beside his window startled the youngster and filled him with dismay. Maybe the bear had somehow gotten up in the tree and was even now looking at him, planning its death-dealing leap to the windowsill. Wanting desperately to flee, but frozen to his bed, the lad shut his eyes, forcing tears down his cheeks. He sat quietly in the dark, a helpless little figure with no hope of rescue. Everyone else was asleep far away down the hall and could never get there in time, so he had to face the beast alone.

The rustling in the tree grew more insistent and the boy braced himself. Then the bear chirped.

It was a soft little sound that didn't quite measure up to what a bear should be saying. Puzzled, but still afraid, the child remained still. The chirp repeated. Then, to the lad's great amazement, the bear broke into song—a beautiful, lilting tune that seemed to transport the night into another place. It spoke of dandelions in the grass, sunshine, dusty bare feet and butterflies on the roses. It didn't sound bear-like at all. Suddenly the boy knew what it was.

Tommy eased out of bed and crept slowly to the window. Straining his eyes in the starlight, he could just barely make out the shape against the skyline. Sure enough, not five feet from his window perched a mockingbird—six ounces of pure music wrapped up in a bunch of feathers, singing its heart out in the face of all the creatures of darkness. Surrounded by the night, not knowing and not caring who was listening, it sang one stanza after another with reckless abandon. On and on the songster trilled as the monsters cringed and slunk away in shame at its glory. Its music transformed the gloom into a soft, warm cloak that welcomed the boy into its protective folds.

Mesmerized by the moment, the child forgot about bears. His heart settled back in his chest, the tears dried, and he grinned. If a little old bird wasn't afraid, then he sure wasn't going to be scared. He was asleep in moments.

Tommy grew up but never forgot the bird. He learned that people everywhere are scared and lonely just as he was that evening, and they need to hear some notes of joy in the gloomy places of their hearts where monsters dwell and the nights get scary. People need to hear the reckless abandon of a free heart singing at the top of its lungs into the faces of all the beasts of despair. So now, wherever he goes, Tommy the grown-up boy makes sure that he does this one thing:

He sings in the dark.

"What's the sense in serving God if nobody knows or cares that you are doing it?"

———•◆•———

For Whom The Toll Is Paid

"Then Moses the servant of the Lord died" *(Deuteronomy 34:5)*. After forty years of being a great leader, the obituary in Deuteronomy called him a servant, almost like serving was more important than leading. Serving wasn't what Moses did for a living; it was who he *was*—his most obvious characteristic. God seemed to be pleased with that. Moses was a good servant, notwithstanding some flaws.

I want to be like Moses, knowing how to serve God and then doing it. I want to be remembered for my serving and I think it will be really fine one day to hear the Lord say, "Well done, good and faithful servant."

I have a problem, though. What does serving God

look like? How do you do it? Half the time I don't know, and the other half, I'm not sure.

A search of the Scriptures helps me clarify it. In every example I can find in the Bible, serving God involves serving people in some way. It's as if you cannot serve God directly; you have to do it through service to His children. John said it bluntly: "The one who does not love his brother whom he has seen, cannot love God whom he has not seen" *(I John 4:20).*

I have determined, then, to serve God in the area of serving other people.

Tomball, Texas boasts a terrific barbecue restaurant. The food is good so the lines are long, and on this day I found myself at the back. Standing in line fails to rank among the top ten exciting things to do, so I cast my eyes about, looking for something to read. On the wall was a framed document listing fifty things you can do to make the day better. I scanned the list.

I drive to work every morning on a toll road and sometimes the tollbooths become backed up. One item on the restaurant list suggested that I pay the toll of the person behind me. My day would be better, it said.

I got excited. I thought, *I can do that! Maybe I can serve God by paying a toll.* So I started a toll-paying crusade.

I considered the idea of going up and down the expressway each day, dispensing little tolls of grace along the road to make the day better for people, serving God in a tangible, visible way. I was curious about the results.

I've paid about ninety tolls now and I've noticed a gradual change of thinking about this campaign.

My first surprise came from the toll recipients: only one acknowledged that I had made his day better. A car pulled up beside me carrying two teen-aged boys grinning and waving. Maybe they were out of money and I had come along in the nick of time. I don't know the reason, but I know that they were the only ones who said "Thanks." All the other vehicles either hung back far behind me or blew past me without the occupants looking at me.

I was angry; discouraged, too. What was wrong with these people? They didn't act like they appreciated my efforts at all. In fact, they acted almost as if I had offended them in some way.

Maybe they thought I wanted something from them, or maybe they just had more important things on their minds. The net result was the same.

I became tired of paying tolls. I was ready to quit this crusade and serve God where people would appreciate it. These people didn't even act as if they knew I was doing something great for God. What's the sense in serving God if nobody knows or cares that you are doing it? It seemed self-defeating.

But then I had a stroke of insight. I quit focusing on how people responded to me and instead turned my attention to how I responded to them. It was fascinating.

Think about it. Whose idea was it to pay the toll in the first place? The other drivers'? Certainly not. It was my idea. I did it voluntarily, presumably with no strings attached.

But if there were no strings attached, then why was I angry? In truth, there were strings attached. I automatically placed conditions upon my acts of grace.

I wanted—and expected—people to appreciate me.

I caught myself looking in the rearview mirror to see the expressions on the people's faces. I was disappointed if there was no one behind me to see me paying his or her toll. I self-consciously glowed when anyone passed me, expecting them to look over and marvel at what a fine fellow I was. Then, when none of it happened as I had expected, I wanted to quit.

Fresh desire turned to tired despair. Has that ever happened to you? Your motives are pure. You yearn to make a difference for God. The plans are laid. The effort is made. But the result is insignificant. It knocks the props out from under you and you want to give up.

But wait a minute.

Who said I should only serve the grateful? Where did I get that idea? Not from Jesus. Where did I learn to think that the blessing of giving is found in receiving? Not from Jesus. Who said I should give grace only to godly, well-behaved people who are polite enough to say "Thank you"? Not Jesus.

For whom do I pay the toll? Paul had a good word for me. He said it like this: "In all the work you are doing, work the best you can. Work as if you were doing it for the Lord, not for people" *(Colossians 3:23)*.

Ah hah! There's my answer. For whom do I pay the toll? For Jesus. If I'm doing work for Jesus Christ, people don't have to thank me; I don't have to be angry if they aren't grateful. I will get sufficient reward from the Lord. It is the Lord Christ I am serving. It is His toll I am paying.

Christ died for us, although we were living against God *(see Romans 5:6)*. Ungodly people can't be depended upon to appreciate grace. They won't act right because they can't act right. There are no guarantees of gratitude. Jesus paid with His life for people like that.

I want it to be said that I was a good servant. "Then Nathan the servant of the Lord died" is an honorable obituary, I think. And I have this hope: when I learn how to give eighty cents as freely as He gave His life, then maybe He will trust me with bigger projects.

"Maybe the discipline, the tears, the hugs, the joy and pain of living in a family are all designed to teach us something."

———•◆•———

She Never Let Go

"Throw him in the pond!"

I listened with delighted anticipation. My eyes were scrunched tightly shut and I felt my body stiffen for the plunge. I heard the air whoosh past my ears on the final dive. But I didn't hit the water because we didn't have any water in our living room, and Mom would never throw me into a pond anyway. She was just saying it because I asked her to. We did it all the time. She would pick me up, swing me around and act like she was throwing me in the pond. But she never let go.

Mom was just like that. When she caught me smoking a cigarette when I was in the fifth grade, she dressed me down good, but she didn't throw me away. When I was supposed to pick a bucket of blackberries, I thought it was too much trouble, so I just stole some of my sister's berries and put them in my bucket. Mom really let me have it, but she didn't let me go. When she said to be home at ten and I barely made it at midnight, she was none too happy, but she didn't give up on me. Through broken bikes, broken arms, broken hearts, and broken dreams, one thing never broke. Mom's love never let go.

Now I wonder what made her that way. You'd think that at some point fatigue would take over, make her too tired, fed up with the grind.

Those who study such things tell us that our views of God are influenced by our views of our parents as we were growing up. Think about it; if you are two years old, who has the ultimate power over you? You certainly don't have control over your own destiny, because without help you wouldn't last a week. Your mom and dad (or other caregivers) maintain absolute authority over you, which makes them the nearest things to God that you can understand. Later, when you learn about a God of the universe—more powerful than your parents are—you naturally think of Him in the same terms as you thought of your parents. If your growing-up experience was a negative one, sometimes it is difficult to envision a compassionate God. However, if your parents modeled a godly life to you, belief in a good God seems to come easier.

Do you think God did that on purpose, making parents look like God to kids? It seems to me that He is using everyday things all the time to give us indications of what He is like, and let me ask you, what is more everyday than a parent? Maybe the discipline, the tears, the hugs, the joy and pain of living in a family are all designed to teach us something.

Listen: "For this reason it is from Him that the whole family of God derives its name, both on earth and in the heavenly realms" *(Ephesians 3:15)*. God apparently has a family, and it sounds like a large one. Maybe His family is like ours, only bigger.

I have a wife of my own now, and she fascinates me. She thinks her God-given role in life is to raise her children. You'd think that at some point fatigue would take over, make her too tired, fed up with the grind.

There is plenty to get tired about. Laundry mounts up; the house gets dirty; bones get broken and ankles get sprained. The list goes on and on, but she never lets go.

In this circle of life we are living, there are lots of repeat scenes. Generation after generation demonstrate the same struggles, the same joys and the same family dynamics. And, as with my mom and my wife, we see God's characteristics lived out in the lives of people in a never-ending stream of evidence.

It's your turn, now. Are you sick of the friend, tired of the boss, bored with the wife, angry at the children? You could easily give up, but what do they need from you? History books are full of blank pages recording the absence of any great event because people gave up too soon. In baseball, you will fail to hit every ball at which you do not swing, and in life you will fail to accomplish every task that you do not pursue to its end. Perseverance will beat out genius every time.

Never let go.

"God's blessings sometimes come in ugly packages. The devil's schemes are invariably gift wrapped. Knowing the difference sets us free."

———•◆•———

Sticks And Snakes

What difference does the truth make?

An earthquake changed the course of the Mississippi River above Memphis, creating a shallow, brush-choked lake. It is known today as Reelfoot Lake.

My friend Phil loves to fish and he hates snakes. Reelfoot Lake has plenty of both. Phil went fishing there and allowed his boat to glide under the shade of a tree. From out of the tree a snake fell into the boat. And into the water jumped Phil. On the way into the water, he started to think: "Let's see, I've just jumped out of a boat with one snake in it, into the water where there are lots of snakes." Consequently, Phil quickly returned to the boat and peeped over the side to see the snake. Much to his amazement, he discovered that the snake was really a stick.

How important is the truth? Phil thinks it is really important to know the difference between a stick and a snake. Not knowing made him jump out of his safe boat into a lake full of snakes.

Did you ever do that?

Church was too boring, so you went to the party instead, where you could have some real fun. Discipline from the old man was too hard to take, so you left the house and hung out with your friends, where you would be accepted for who you are. Your wife has lost her appeal, so you search the field for more charming women. The teacher tries to give you advice on life, but she is either too old or too young, too black or too white, too fat or too skinny, too educated or too uneducated, too flawed in too many other ways for you to listen to her, so you make the same mistakes all over again.

Sticks and snakes. They are everywhere. It is possible to live our whole lives not knowing the difference and then wonder why everything turns out wrong.

What would you give to know the real truth? Sometimes snakes charm you, and sticks appear menacing. What a relief it would be to know the difference. Where can we get glasses that will fix our blurred vision?

Jesus said it like this: "If you continue in My word, then you are truly disciples of Mine; and you will know the truth, and the truth will make you free" *(John 8:31-32)*.

What's that you say about the truth? I really *can* know it? I really *can* learn to recognize snakes posing as sticks, wolves in sheeps' clothing, saints in beggars' clothes, cries for help in defiant shouting? Yes.

God's blessings sometimes come in ugly packages. The devil's schemes are invariably gift-wrapped. Knowing the difference sets us free.

That's a beautiful promise, being set free. How does knowledge of the truth set us free?

The worst kind of slavery happens inside our heads. Worry that it won't turn out like we had hoped: slavery. Anger at knowing we could fix it if we could control it, but we can't control it: slavery. Depression from the pitiful realization that society has huge problems and we are too small to make a difference: slavery. Fear at knowing that, no matter what we do, we are going to die: slavery.

What does the truth have to do with it? Simply this: the truth is better news than the lie. And what is the real truth?

Well, it might not turn out as we had hoped, but it will be what we need, so we can quit worrying: freedom.

We can't control it, therefore we can't fix it, but our Father does control it and He will fix it, so we can quit being angry: freedom. Society has big problems and we are small, but society changes in small increments and we can do our part, so we can quit being depressed: freedom. No matter what we do, we are going to die, but we are the children of the eternal King and the day we die will be better than the day we were born, so we can quit being fearful: freedom.

How does the truth set us free? At the very least, it sets us free from the worry, anger, depression, and fear that comes from believing things that are not true.

Sticks and snakes don't have to worry us, because we can learn to tell the difference. He said we would. What a wonderful promise.

"Being dough in the hands of a master baker is torturous. Later, though, you really shine."

———•◦•———

Bread Not Quite Done

Early in the morning is the best time to go. Not many cars are out yet, so the drive is peaceful. By 6:30 the doors to the coffee shop have been open an hour and a half, and even without the brightly lit sign you would know you were there. The aroma of fresh-baked bread and coffee permeates the air and leads you by the nose.

Inside, racks of multiple varieties of breads are stacked in neat little rows behind the glass. Employees stand ready at the counter to take your order. It's the same every day. No matter what type of bread you order, it is invariably baked to perfection, sweet to the palate and satisfying to the appetite.

The bread is recently baked, judging by the scent. Someone was probably busy over an oven, kneading, twisting, stirring, mixing, pounding, and ultimately baking all the tasty tidbits that eventually become displays to the public, available for consumption. It's hard to believe that such delicate morsels could have been merely shapeless lumps of dough not long ago.

I'm wondering something now: at what point does dough become bread? When does bread really become bread?

Bread doesn't start out being baked and under glass ready to eat. In various stages of its development, it is hardly recognizable as bread at all. Is it actually bread when it is just dough?

What if it is partly cooked, but not done? Do you know the kind I mean? The type with the sticky middle that clings to the top of your mouth. Few things are more aggravating than biting into a perfect-looking roll and getting stuck to the goo inside. Bread not quite done is nasty. But is it bread?

At what point does bread really become bread? Is it bread while it is grain standing in the field? Is it bread when it is flour? What about when it is dough? Or, is it bread only after it comes out of the oven perfect, without a sticky middle?

It's hard to say. I think the question is best answered by the baker.

"Mr. Baker, I see you have a big mess here. What are you doing?"

"I'm baking bread."

"Well, when will it become bread?"

"It's already bread; it just isn't done yet."

The baker really believes that it is bread all along; it is just not finished bread. It isn't done until the baker takes it out of the oven and says it is ready, but the baker is not upset because wheat hasn't become a bagel yet, or because dough doesn't look like a glazed croissant. He isn't mad because flour doesn't look like toast. Let's ask him one more question.

"Tell me, Mr. Baker, what do you have to do to this shapeless lump in order to make it look like bread?"

"Well, I have to beat it up, twist it around and around, fold it back over itself, squash it flat, cut it up in little pieces, and then subject it to intense heat for a period of time. Then it'll be done."

Hmmm . . . how would you like to be bread? Would you want a baker to work on you? Being dough in the hands of a master baker is torturous. Later, though, you really shine. Later, you are more palatable. Later, the value of the pain becomes evident.

I'm God's croissant, and I'm not quite done. He is my Baker, and He will tell me when I'm finished *(see Hebrews 12:2)*. In the meantime, I do what undone bread does. I irritate people when they take a close look at me and see my sticky middle. I am unattractive because I've been beat up, cut up, smashed flat, and twisted around. Oftentimes, I feel like I'm in the fire.

What do dough and I have in common? We are both bread in the making. We are both unattractive to an untrained eye. Neither one of us looks like we have much value. But is that true?

Can a baker be pleased with plain dough? Sure. Can God be pleased with me? Sure.

How?

The baker knows that each phase of the bread's creation is perfectly acceptable, and he is willing to work patiently with dusty flour and sticky goo until he gets a completed product. He believes that with patience he can make something wonderful from a shapeless lump; a creation he had in mind before he even mixed the dough.

God is doing the same with you and me. He thinks we are perfectly acceptable, even with all our imperfections, and He knows He can make something wonderful of us, creations that He had in mind before we ever existed. The apostle Paul said it like this: "He who began a good work in you will perfect it until the day of Christ Jesus" *(Philippians 1:6)*. I'm not perfect yet, but I am in a perfect process.

Only after Jesus looks us in the eye and says, "Well done" *(Matthew 25:21)*, will we be complete. Until then, we are still in the oven, cooking.

"An air of being lost surrounded her in a veil of isolation through which no one, it seemed, could reach her."

Crying Over Lost Clothes

I was there to pick her up for an appointment as promised, but I hadn't scheduled time to wait and watch her cry. There she sat nevertheless, tears of helpless grief tracing the well-traveled furrows of her cheeks, slipping silently off her chin to splash onto wrinkled hands clasped nervously in her lap.

Sixty-eight winters had blown their cold winds at her and as many seasons of sunshine had smiled upon her youth, her marriages, her children, furs, houses, jewels and riches, and now, her despair. An air of being lost surrounded her in a veil of isolation through which no one, it seemed, could reach her.

We'll call her Lois, but it doesn't matter what her name was. There was nothing remarkable about her appearance. She bore the stamp of old age, but not glaringly so. Her face was stern and she looked like she had worn the cloak of authority in the past. She wasn't lovely to look at or talk to. The only notable quality was her voice, a high-pitched, self-pitying whine that bespoke her hopelessness.

"I'm so worried about my clothes." The statement emanated in a half-wail, reminding me of a spoiled child asking for something that she has given up all hope of getting, but thinking for some reason that she should keep on begging.

The situation was not really critical, from my viewpoint. Here we both were, sitting in the little room that she called home. Everything that the lady had kept from her previous life was here: a couch, a few personal things, and a suit or two of clothes in the closet. She did have additional garments at another home from which she had recently moved, and it was these that worried her. She believed that she couldn't go with me to her appointment because those clothes weren't here.

I divined a simple answer: I would go get the clothes for her the first thing tomorrow morning. For now, she had plenty to wear so she had no reason to worry. With those assurances, she should be perfectly content. I told her so. "Lois, I'll get those clothes for you tomorrow." That should do it.

It didn't.

"But what about my clothes?" I thought she hadn't heard me. What did she mean? I didn't have time to play games with this woman. I was in the business of helping people, and I was trying to help her, so she needed to get with the program.

I tried it again.

"Lois, you don't have to worry about your clothes. I promise that I will get them for you." I thought that if I promised, she would believe me. After all, I was telling her the truth. She should be able to see that and quit questioning me.

"Yeah, but I'm so worried about my clothes." This was wearing thin. Her high-pitched whine, my tight schedule, her reluctance to get out of bed, and her helpless attitude all combined to wear a hole in my already threadbare patience. I was used to helping people who would receive my help. Who did she think I was, anyway? I wasn't just some nobody off the street. I was a businessman, a man of truth, a man on a mission to help. Yes, I was important, someone to whom she should listen. Surely she was smart enough to figure that out.

Then why did she ask again, and again, and ten more times? I couldn't give her enough assurance to comfort her. No matter how many times or how many ways I told her that she didn't have to worry, she could not believe it. She just kept repeating her problem. "I don't know what I'll do without my clothes."

I wanted to scream at her, jam the truth down her throat, make her take it no matter how it tasted. I wanted to yell at her in a stew of outrage and frustration, "Lois, why in the world won't you believe me? It would do you so much good if you would just believe. I'm telling you the truth but you won't hear it. I'm offering you help but you won't take it. I'm telling you things that would give you life but you insist on staying dead!"

I was purple with self-righteous indignation because Lois wouldn't do as I wanted. Then it hit me. What this lady was doing to me, I had done to God. Before I believed Him, I had questions.

"I'm so worried, who will take care of me?" I asked in deep dismay.

He answered just as I had answered Lois. "I will," He replied.

"Yes, but my problems are big. Who will take care of me, really?"

"I will," said He.

"But you don't understand. I need help. I'm so worried about it all."

I suppose God would have said the same to me. "Nathan, why in the world won't you believe Me?! It would do you so much good if you would just believe."

We wept together, the lady and I, and my anger went away. Then she let me in.

The veil lifted for a moment, the hard shell cracked a little, and her words spoke volumes: "I'm really not used to anybody actually doing what they said they would do."

Lord, help me. She needs from me the same things I need from You. Dependability. Integrity. Truth.

And above all, compassion when I don't believe.

"Deep within your mind, planted early and growing slowly among the hot cotton fields, the abject poverty, and the southern rebel social isolation (the Civil War is still fresh on the minds of your kin), a question arises in your mind and finally blossoms into words. Where is God?"

Cotton Pickin'

South Alabama in summertime is hot. Then comes cotton-picking time and it gets hotter.

The sweat starts on your face and trickles down your chin, gathering moisture as it goes. Your shirt gets wet, then your pants, and finally it feels like sweat is filling up your shoes and making them heavy, provided you have any shoes on.

The chances of having any shoes on are slim if you are thirteen years old, the son of a disabled father, and it is 1936. In fact, the chances of having anything at all beyond the bare necessities are pretty remote.

You start picking once the dew is off the cotton boles, and you are grateful that you have an easy job: You didn't have to start work at daylight like most folks you know. Your back is loose early on and you make good time. The cotton comes off easily in your hands, and you drop it lightly into the sack that you drag behind you by a strap on your shoulder. It's a pretty day, your wage of fifty cents per hundred pounds of cotton is good, and you are full of the vigor of youth.

By midday, you have lost most of your vigor, your bag's strap has gouged a hole in your shoulder, and you have worn out every comfortable position there is for picking cotton, namely, bending over, walking on your knees, and scooting on your seat.

Along about mealtime the dinner bell rings, and you go eat at the landowner's table. He eats a lot better than you do at home, so you thoroughly enjoy your meal, not wasting a scrap.

After dinner, it's back to the cotton field where the afternoon sun beats on you like a glowing anvil, and you pray for a cloud or sunset, whichever comes first. Finally, the evening dew signals the end of your working day, and you walk home to your house that, although poor, is better than the log cabin you were born in.

The next day you do it again, or go to work for someone else plowing his mules, or hoeing his corn, or feeding his hogs, or whatever you can find to do.

You don't have much of your own, because your Mom and Dad are poor. Your Dad is laid up crippled; your Mom tries to make do. You don't have shoes very often, so it's good that you live where it is warm. You don't have good medical care, as evidenced by a toe that never healed correctly after you nearly cut it off with an ax. You don't have much of a social life, believing that most strangers are out to take advantage of you. The list of have-nots is a lot longer than the haves. It will still be some time before you see your first twenty-dollar bill, but you did find a fifty-cent piece one time in a blackberry patch. You took it home, delighted. It proved its worth by providing for a gallon of cottonseed cooking oil that your family had been needing.

Times are hard by most standards, but you don't know it because you were born into hard times. You think that's how they are supposed to be. Looking back, you know you were poor because the Great Depression was in full swing at the time, but it had not changed your lifestyle one bit.

Somewhere you have heard that all things work together for good for those who love the Lord, and you are wondering if that message has anything to do with you, or does it just apply to rich folks. You doubt that the message is for you because God probably doesn't even know where South Alabama is.

Deep within your mind, planted early and growing slowly among the hot cotton fields, the abject poverty, and the southern rebel social isolation (the Civil War is still fresh on the minds of your kin), a question arises in your mind and finally blossoms into words.

Where is God?

The question haunts you and drives you to the Bible. It compels you to learn and do and discuss and experience, to ask more questions and seek deeper understanding until, sixty years later, you know the answer.

Gathered with your family in the living room, with your wife, all five children, their husbands and wives and their children, you talk about it. You talk about where God is.

He's been there all along.

God is in the cotton fields, in the songs and stories of the Negroes who work the fields beside you. He is at the dining table of the landowner as you bow your weary head to give thanks. God is in the faded shirts of the men, shirts that show the outline of their overall suspenders, only now the men aren't wearing overalls because they are at church. He is in the song of the mockingbird that interrupts your bedtime prayers by singing all night in the apple tree.

And, God is at work in you to make all things work together for good.

During the hard times, the times of the have-nots, forces were at work that you didn't know anything about. Forces that, in due time, would allow you to see more of the world than most people ever see, forces that would provide you with a college education, a faithful wife, children, a farm, a career, a good name among men of standing. Forces without and within, molding you, shaping your character, driving you to excel, to be more than your beginning.

Now you see it. With the clarity hindsight brings, you see "the plan" behind it all. You see the coincidences that weren't coincidental. You see the discouraging failures that weren't failures at all, but were simply hints to change directions. You see the lost opportunities, the hardships, the poverty, and even the cotton fields, as clear evidence of a Divine hand at work, not to destroy you, but to create you. To create you into a tool useful for His service.

How many people have you led to God because of your hardship? How many people have come to know Jesus because of your character, a character that could only develop through much labor? How many lives have been touched by your presence, your perseverance, your high moral standards, your dedication to your God, all of which might not have been yours had you not suffered?

It has been God who has been at work in you all along,

to make things work together for good, both yours and untold numbers of other people.

South Alabama is hot in the summertime, without a doubt. But I am eternally grateful that, during the summer of 1936, in spite of the heat, a thirteen-year-old boy went ahead and worked anyway, and worked the next year too, and the next. He grew and developed and, quite by accident I am sure, became who he is: A man of God, a man who has lived successfully, a man of reputation among men of good standing, a man in deed. A man who is, I am delighted to say...

My Dad.

"Most of us, at some level, want to be good."

———•◦•———

God In Common Places

Those people who rank as heroes are few and far be tween. Most of the rest of us live ordinary lives, dwell in ordinary houses, have ordinary jobs and children, and encounter ordinary pleasures and problems. We live out the commonplace among common people engaged in common activities.

We need a God who is comfortable in common places. If our God lived only on mountaintops, or in elaborate houses, or in beautiful people, then most of us would never find Him. We need a God who dwells among the common folk.

Listen to this. "In the beginning was the Word, and the Word was with God and the Word was God ... And the Word became flesh, and dwelt among us" *(John 1:1, 14)*."

What a message. God among us. Who is a God like that, who will mingle with people? Why, in fact, do we need that?

Most of us yearn to be better. Most of us dream of greater accomplishments. Most of us have within us a spiritual sensitivity, a vague knowledge that there is a greater good somewhere, and we aren't it. Most of us, at some level, want to be good.

Why do we need God among us? Because the truth is, in spite of our noble ambitions to be good, most of us live our ordinary lives knowing that we aren't good. We need help.

We need to see God in common places. We need to look at the stars tonight and see a huge, organized power at work, then look at the sunrise tomorrow morning and recognize the consummate skill of a master artist. We need to hear a bird singing and be delighted with God as a musician, then wave at our neighbor and know God as a lover of people. Then we need to see a beggar and be reminded of the grace of God, and then go to a coffee shop to be filled with the bread of life.

When we do meet Him and—most importantly—recognize Him, then we begin an amazing trip. We don't have to leave the neighborhood, but we travel just the same. Our journey takes us down a road of change, and the closer we walk with this God-of-Common-Places, the more we evolve.

It's like a metamorphosis. The ordinary caterpillar isn't just a worm anymore; it's a potential butterfly. And, that pesky child you thought was just a burden? He's a potential judge of angels *(I Corinthians 6:3)*. The beggar on the street? He might be God's messenger in disguise. And, most amazingly, we the common folk aren't so common anymore. We are children of the King.

Christ at the Coffee Shop. God in Common Places. I hope that His presence in your life will allow you to go about your days in delighted wonder, with new eyes perceiving a divine hand at work in ordinary circumstances, among ordinary people and within you.

The End